Work on the Mountain

Other Books by N.V.M. Gonzalez

The Winds of April
Seven Hills Away
A Season of Grace
The Bamboo Dancers
Look, Stranger, on this Island Now
Mindoro and Beyond
The Bread of Salt and Other Stories

Work on the Mountain

N. V. M. GONZALEZ

Introduction by OSCAR V. CAMPOMANES

**With " 'As in Myth, the Signs Were All Over':
The Fiction of N. V. M. Gonzalez"
by RICHARD R. GUZMAN**

UNIVERSITY OF THE PHILIPPINES PRESS
1995

ISBN-971-542-063-X

Editorial and Production Supervision by
Laura L. Samson and Nelia L. Gahol
Photography by N. V. M. Gonzalez
Cover Design by June Poticar Dalisay
Book Design by Linda T. Lingbaoan-Bulong
Set in Gatineau, Antique Olive and Linus

Printed in the Philippines by Kayumanggi Press

Contents

Introduction

N.V.M. Gonzalez and the Archipelagic Poetics of Filipino Postcoloniality

Oscar V. Campomanes

Nakurang ti pammatina iti iliw. [He has little faith in the power of longing.]

—Pelagio Halaba

So primary is homesickness as a motive for writing fiction, so powerful the yearning to memorialize what we've lived, inhabited, been hurt by and loved, that the impulse often goes unacknowledged.

—Joyce Carol Oates

A U.S.-based critic once upbraided N.V.M. Gonzalez and Bienvenido Santos for seeking "roots in a bygone rural Philippines seen from the eyes of a Hemingway or Katherine Anne Porter—a rural space no longer mapped by American anthropologists like Alfred Kroeber or Felix Keesing, but by insurgents." Recently, the same critic, now an "ethnic" literature specialist, denounced N.V.M. for "the integrationist 'melting pot' tendencies that vitiate [his] works." To illustrate his precipitate claims, our critic briefly invoked a "typical" Gonzalez story in which N.V.M., now dismissed as "petit-bourgeois expatriate," presumably makes "the sublimating images of an archaic economy survive."

For every denunciation like this critic's, there are mountains of attentive and sympathetic exegetical prose produced by Philippine colleagues out of N.V.M.'s extensive oeuvre. Guzman's brilliant essay, included in this collection, is a most refreshing addition to this critical archive. It is therefore far from my intention to mount a defense on N.V.M.'s behalf. N.V.M. does not need one. Any reader who carefully scours the scope of N.V.M.'s literary achievements in Filipino literary history, and discerns the startling cultural designs out of the totality of his creative endeavors, will find that N.V.M.'s complex ideas and positions are irreducible to our critic's shifting charges.

Colonial pedagogy has historically placed Filipino English writers like N.V.M., and their postcolonial confreres elsewhere, in the difficult position of negotiating between "folklore and the technical dazzle of the metropolis," a condition so overheated that they not infrequently turned to "a cultural miscellany based on Empire" for their literary creations (Timothy Brennan; Frantz Fanon). N.V.M., however, presents a remarkable exception from Brennan's Fanonian prototype of "the colonial artist" who—because of the decolonizing search for roots and "a more congenial national origin than provided by colonial history" (Edward Said)—created literary folklorism or nativisms which "had the potential for being only the reverse side of assimilationism, equally alienated, equally outside looking in."

One cannot read the deceptively nativist depictions of *kainginero* "grace" or peasant survivalism in N.V.M.'s extended/ short fiction without considering their productive qualifications and equally poetic (but historicized) sublations in N.V.M., literary essays and cultural criticism (a retrospective sampling of which is presented here). Critics like Leonard Casper and Miguel Bernad who reduce N.V.M., literary geography into a valorization of the primordial "Filipino," or the Marxist-progressivist critic who dismisses it as a naturalistic representation of an "archaic economy," share the common guilt of judging Filipino literature and history from a Eurocentric perspective; either the *grand récit* of the post-Enlightenment, or the "great modes-of-production narrative [of a] transition from feudalism to capitalism (Gayatri Spivak). Guzman's luminous reading of N.V.M.'s narrative style as "deemphasiz[ing] the forward-moving, linear, in favor of a complex, often near-static time frame, a frame which shimmers gently as Gonzalez moves easily, with minimal transitions, between past, present, future, between conscious time and the less-metered times of memory, dream, hallucination, or reflection" provides more productive critical cues.

We need to recognize the critical and political power of "the new territoriality" in writing like N.V.M.'s (Said), the immensely enabling and psychically nurturing values of its conjunctural and "strategic essentialism" (Spivak) for the postcolonial predicament. Filipinos still confront the literally and figuratively dislocating effects of the Philippine's multiple colonizations (Spain, United States, Japan, neocolonial US dependency): over six millions in 140 countries, according to the latest estimates, including the hundreds of thousands more who are displaced from the various Philippine provinces and now crowd Metro Manila's slums and hovels. (Manila-centrism and corrupt post-independence regimes constitute as much of a historical scourge as foreign colonial invasions.) The critical emergence and revaluation of Filipino English and "Filipino American" writing (categories which N.V.M.'s career traverses) in Philippine nationalist discourses and current "global" conversations on postcolonialism (or the aftermath of various post-Columbian EuroAmerican colonialism) is vexed by several social-historical preconditions.

Filipino nationalist critique, with its empowering with the native-vernacular, remains unable to recognize the antecedent and the analogue of the Filipino "abroad" (the nomadic colonial subject) in the "stay-at-home Filipino" who, by circumstances of history and biography, has chosen to write in the colonial languages. For writers like N.V.M. and Santos who literally experienced this "alienated" plight and outsiderhood through "the manipulations of extended residence in the metropole" (N.V.M.'s own words), the convergence of linguistic and actual displacements could not but both burden and distinguish their cultural products. "To be a writer in English is already to be socially specified" (Raymond Williams): a condition of difference from one's less privileged kindred that invites symbolic, poignant, and often adversely-received attempts at identification with one's Others and beloved *heimat*. This dialectic between language and place/displacement or identity is common to all writing produced in previously- and neo-colonized regions in the world according to theorists of postcolonial literatures and discourse.

With the "receiving" of English during the U.S. colonial period (Gonzalez), the Filipino writer was converted into "a domestic exile, an expatriate who has not left his homeland" (Wilfrido Nolledo). What has been discerned, in the recurrent thematics of rootlessness in *ilustrado* and modern Filipino diasporic writing, as "a spiritual dislocation which is nurtured by the act of writing in a foreign language," finds its historical virtuality *in* the difficult space of diasporic distances inhabited by colonial-language and itinerant writers (David Quemada; Benedict Anderson). The many nuances of this extra/territorial poetics, "the primacy of the geographical" or the "cartographic impulse" (Said) in postcolonial discourse and texts, surely survive caricaturish reductions. But one cannot over-appreciate the fact of "a pressing need for the recovery of the land that, because of the presence of the colonizing outsider [and one's displacements abroad], is recoverable at first only through the imagination" (Said). Now potentially dismissible (by the increasingly unproblematized obsession with "lost" vernacular traditions and regional literatures) as an "archaic" remnant or survival of "bygone" American Empire Days, (post)colonial Filipino language-writing has been unable to find a "home" in the fashionable Western academic cottage-industry of postcolonial studies either. If you're not Anglophone or Francophone, then tough luck. The saga of Filipino postcolonial displacements continues.

The peculiar American publishing history of Filipino writers has never ceased to intrigue me. Although Santos's short fiction has been internationally anthologized and N.V.M.'s writing has been translated into Malaysian and Russian, Filipino writers who looked or migrated to "America" for international recognition and in search of a "world audience," have had mixed or little success (an impetus hardly monopolized by Filipino writers; expectant writers from the provinces of European Empires in the Americas, Africa, and Asia typically moved to the metropolitan capitals for exilic haven, education, publishing, and political agitation for national independence). It took the genesis and emergence of a Filipino American immigrant presence in the United States and the 1960s "yellow power" movements spearheaded by rebellious Asian/Filipino American youth— tired of having their American nativity questioned by Anglo-Americans—to initiate the conditions for the recuperation of Bulosan's *America Is in the Heart* (1946) in 1973, and eventually, the retrospective publication of Santos's *Scent of Apples* (1979) and Gonzalez' *The Bread of Salt and Other Stories* (1993) by a U.S. university press. There are notable exceptions, like the early triumphs of Jose Garcia Villa, Carlos Bulosan, Stevan Javellana, Wilfrido Nolledo, and recently,

Ninotchka Rosca and Jessica Hagedorn; but, as in the case of all exceptions, they remain precarious.

A Filipino writer, who recently and quite obviously benefited from these U.S. conjunctural developments in having one of his "epic" novellas published by a major New York publishing house, declared to me and a mortified dinner audience a few weeks ago that this Filipino submergence is attributable to a lack of Filipino "originality," the "derivative-ness" of Filipino literature. This in itself is an "unoriginal" re-hearsal of recurrent claims by a powerful genealogy of U.S. colonial discourses: from Arthur Stanley Riggs to Sidney Hook and John Leonard in literary criticism, that "there is no Fili-pino literature" (or if there is anything of the sort, it is but a tropical copycat of original Anglo-American canons); from John R.M. Taylor to Stanley Karnow and Glenn May in his-toriography, that there has never been such an entity as a Filipino nation; from Dean Worcester who popularized turn-of-the-century images of Filipinos as mix of untamed tribes inhabiting uncharted jungles, to an unidentified Harvard Uni-versity professor who advised a Chicano anthropologist in the 1960s to reconsider his idea of conducting fieldwork in the Philippines because the Filipinos are "a people without culture."

I prefer N.V.M.'s historicizing analysis of this paradoxical desire of Filipino writers to be recognized for the cultural distinctiveness of their writing by the very same exclusive circles of "American" and international literary celebrity which were to dismiss Filipino colonials as mimics and ever-inadequate facsimiles. N.V.M., in one of his more compelling excavations of the effects of colonial history on Filipino politics and cultures, calls it "the Jones Law Syndrome." The Jones Law of 1916 was a colonial piece of legislation which deferred Philippine decolonization by enforcing a continuing period of American tutelage in liberal democracy and "rep-resentative government." This was the American colonial state's response to persisting Filipino nationalist demands for independence. But after 1916, "the solicitation of foreign, and generally American, approval" became both a "national habit" and a matter of "national character." In the political realms, several lobbying teams were dispatched to Washington as generally circumscribed "independence missions" until the 1930s (Bernadita Reyes-Churchill), while in the literary-cultural realm, the likes of Jose Garcia Villa headed for the mythic American publishing capital of New York.

To this explanation, I can only add the underappreciated Philippine misfortune of colonization by Western powers whose imperial-national rhetorics and politics continue to treat the archipelago as an "anomalous" event in their "otherwise glorious" global conquests: a wart, a disfiguration, and a source of national shame that demands to be hidden from the world and their own citizens. For Spain, it was the unbearable humiliation of effectively losing its last Crown Colony to the 1896-98 Revolution of its *indios del este* even as Spain had historically considered *Las Islas Filipinas* as a remote outpost, an administrative nightmare, and an unprofitable venture compared to its American territories. For the United States, it is the ignoble and forgettable memory of the Philippine-American War, presumably a "great aberration" in the history of U.S. expansionism (Samuel Flagg Bemis) and considered by U.S. textbook wisdom as a "shadowy anti-climax" to the "splendid little war" with Spain, the "brief but victorious military romp" which hugs the central space for accounts of that American historical moment (Daniel Boone Schirmer).

In the extended essays gathered for this retrospective volume, N.V.M. offers us a modular and nomadic miscellany of his making as a writer and as a Filipino "in the world." His story is also our story, the millions of us who long for "home" and yet must remain where we are due to all kinds of extenuating circumstances. One would wish, contra the Jones Law Syndrome, that this volume would be simultaneously published abroad and become available well beyond its intended Philippine audiences. Raging debates in U.S. and

Western academies over the Age of Empires (Eric Howbs-bawm) and its fateful aftermaths have much to learn from the Philippine experience. These discussions, anchored mostly by "native" intellectuals emerging out of the British and French colonial traditions, are agitated by two things: the despotic character of ethnic nationalisms and post-imperial class/caste élite-dominated nation-states (the Balkans only present the most pressing case which have caused tremendous human suffering and massacres; and, the cosmopolitan desire for cultural hybridity and border-crossings, for the barely-glimpsed "history of the possible" (David Lloyd), for those yet unimagined forms of human communication and community which can break down the terrifying claims of cultural and political monisms. (As the collapse of socialist state-building experiments and the Berlin Wall bears out, even proletarian utopias no longer offer viable alternatives).

The Philippines have survived and persisted through what N.V.M. calls a "lahar of colonizations"—among his more recent and startling critical-poetic deployments of the "native" landscape's aspects—and their own nightmarish experiences of forging a nation-state out of a dizzying multitudes of islands, peoples, and cultures. (The Marcos dictatorship is not a distant memory.) Who would not learn from the examples of such memorable Filipino literary characters as Doro and Sabel in *A Season of Grace* who, with nimbleness of feet, hop from kaingin to kaingin, and season to season, to beat the fates, or the paternally benign demands of semifeudal over-lords? Other Filipino writers, following N.V.M., have created equally compelling models of what the native American writer Gerald Vizenor would recognize as the difficult art of "survivance" amidst the most inhospitable environments and historical tribulations: the "iron-haired women squatting at street corners" of Ninotchka Rosca's re-imagined Manila, who fan and vend delicious "corn still sizzling from the red-eyed coals" even as a new war yet again embroils the archipelago (*State of War*, 1988); or Jose Dalisay's ironic-minded Noel Bu-laong who "kills time in a warm place" and who, from the perspective of an itinerant repatriate, critically recalls a time when Marcos was "father to us all" (1992).

Filipinos are no strangers to the now presumably epochal experience of migration and crossings across national frontiers. Long before other postcolonial writers began to hew a powerful theoretics of transnational migrancy and Chicano writers articulated a "border aesthetics," N.V.M. was already fashioning a Filipino nomadology—what Carlos Bulosan in the wonderful story "Be American" called the "law of the nomad"—in early stories like "Far Horizons" (one of my Gonzalez favorites); in paradigmatic characters like the hope-less peripatetic Ernie Rama in *The Bamboo Dancers*; in catalytic deployments, though his fiction and literary-critical essays, of powerful "archipelagic images" from his Mindoro and Romblon islander past like its *kaingins*, its *batels*, its promising but dangerous oceanic vistas, and its mobile and portable Hanunóo *kalutang* music. This Filipino nomadology —a creative response to the archipelagic and ethnolinguistic diversity of the country, its unusual series of colonial incarce-rations, and the ultimate (im)possibility of Philippine nation-building given its ever-interrupted histories—has many literary elaborations.

When Filipinos "abroad" repossess the Philippines in their discourses of nostalgia or their cultural texts, it is usually a Philippines that displays the virtues of the local and the locale. Think of Santos's Sulucan or Albay; Linda Ty-Casper's Manila standing in the accumulated silences of centuries, a Manila even different from Jessica Hagedorn's seething cauldron of social conflict, or Rosca's metropolis resiliently rising through layers of war-induced destruction and rebirth; Michelle Skinner's deromanticized Olongapo, with its children in "oversized T-shirts"; Cecilia Brainard's Cebu (Ubec) with its sedimented histories of folklore and urban influences. In Filipino English literature, Manuel Arguilla's bucolic Nagreb-can and Sinai Hamada's fog-kist Northern highlands are only among many notable instances.

While American colonialists and ethnographers tended to dismiss Filipino localistic politics and imaginaries as a problem of Filipino regionalism (sometimes "tribalism")—like it were a cultural DNA encoded in native genes—this localization is probably the most interesting Philippine *historical* contribution to current critiques of nationalism. For Filipinos, *Las Filipinas* never really had any one center (although Manila and the Tagalogs often aspired to the privileged status) but possess local, specific, and shifting contours, depending on the beholder. What Filipinos and writers like N.V.M. seek to imagine, it seems, is a nation that is not like most nations we see today. It is a nation of fluid, shifting communities whose tendencies toward decentering and pluralism provide the kernels for powerful autocritiques of grand narratives— narratives whose nationalist ambitions we now see in border-skirmishes, ethnic cleansing, white-supremacist movements, and corrupt bureaucratic state structures.

The cartographic impulse of exilic and postcolonial writing—the repossession of a "poetically projected base"— enables not only a whole set of "assertions, recoveries, and identifications" against colonial legacies, but also a "new pantheon of heroes, myths, and religions" for the decolonizing effort (Said). N.V.M.'s own imaginative geography of an alternative nation, as the following essays should show, already offers the archipelagic and nomadic poetics which would allow "the fragility of mornings in *this* country" (Ninotchka Rosca) to retain its refreshing evanescence in a world increasingly terrorized by apocalyptic and terminal visions of history and peoplehood.

August 30, 1995
Oakland, California

Preface

Tiger at Ajanta

*J*t was about 200 B.C., in Maharashtra State, in Central India, that a community of Buddhist monks began building
Ajanta. For almost a thousand years, they dug and carved out
of the sides of a steep ravine about thirty caves and temple
halls, leaving besides a gallery of frescoes and sculptures that
continue to beggar the imagination to this day.

The work was completed circa 650 A.D. For centuries this
legacy was lost to the world: the jungle is never ill-disposed
to take over. But then one day, in 1819, a tiger emerged from
behind a tangle of vines in the area and by sheer happen-
stance came in the sight of a British soldier's rifle. Before he
could fire, however, it vanished and was never seen again.

It was in the fall of 1962 that I learned about Ajanta. The
site was one of several places that the Indian government
invited a group of us Filipino writers, sculptors and painters
to visit. While sharing the experience of colonialism, although
under different systems, India and the Philippines were barely
getting acquainted with each other at this point in time. Any
diligent student of the Philippines's status as an American
cultural dependency can handily tell you why; but to none of
us that had been invited to visit India that year did our
cultural innocence appear to be a problem. There were ten of

us altogether; and we were oh, so ignorant about India—perhaps in a teenage sort of way.

The trip. though, was exciting in itself. Although it had been already several months after the Sino-Indian border conflict, anti-Chinese sentiment was still rampant in Calcutta, our first stop. To this day I still recall the near-disaster we ran into when a group of curious bystanders mistook us for Chinese.

I had joined three painter friends on their first outdoor sketching session that morning, and a crowd quickly collected around us. We thought, well, it is good to provide people some diversion. In a few minutes, however, loud threats could be heard, and while we understood not one word of Bengali, there was no mistaking the meaning of those noises and angry gestures.

Our worst fears were confirmed when several men started to overturn our car that had been parked at the curb. Anything could have happened had not two gendarmes came to our rescue. "These are Filipinos, and our guests!" or words to that effect, was the explanation given; but the soldiers were scarcely convincing. Amidst much shoving and grumbling, we managed to quit the premises, with one soldier on each side of our car, standing at ready on the running board. The ashram that had served for our quarters was ten long minutes away. Small hostile-looking groups tried to block us at nearly every corner.

The visit to Agra and Delhi three days later did not restore our shattered nerves, what with the heat exacerbating the situation. It was not until after the long train journey south to Bombay that we began to heal. After the plane ride to Maharashtra State and, eventually, our sampling of the Ajanta cave-temples, we probably were recovered fully, collectively speaking; but sampling is the only suitable word, because that was all we could do. I relate these details to highlight, as a matter of fact my slow grasp of the significance of Ajanta. Perhaps the encounter at the park had been meant to remind us of our fervid quest for identity.

Unlike the tiger that vanished in the wink of an eye, my

experience of Ajanta has stayed with me for years. I remember entering one of the large cave temples: a path beneath a waterfall leads to it. With the sputter, indeed, still on our arms and faces, we reach a large prayer hall. There we come upon two benches that are empty but there is a feeling that they are to be occupied shortly. The feeling grows as it dawns on us that at our back is a choirloft with banisters. Could it be that singing is about to begin? We wait and look around; the ceiling is markedly arched and our line of sight is quietly directed toward a Buddha figure at the far end of the hall. At this time of day, a beam of sunlight has descended upon the head: it is pointless to be awed any further! There is enough wonder here to last a lifetime. The Buddha's lips have broken into a smile...

I've brought home from Ajanta also a sense of fullness and the oneness of things. For this is the message inscripted in the frescoes, and the ample walls of the cave temples appear to have taken the vegetable dyes and colors so well. Time seems to have done little to diminish the love of life that the ravishing and voluptuous men and women of that age celebrated and now invite us to share.

Perhaps the meaning I am giving Ajanta, my sense that it is as quintessential a metaphor as any for the writer's task, is too idiosyncratic, even perverse. But countless have been the times when my memory of those cave temples so inspired my writing that I feel certain that the only logical and honest way an artist may deal with Reality is to aspire to the dedication and faith of those workers at Ajanta. How fortunate of that one monk, perhaps the last of several who had been committed to the task, into whose cubicle a tiger once turned for shelter and safety.

To the U.P. College of Arts and letters, the Department of English, and the Creative Writing Center grateful thanks are due for making available in one volume the materials that follow. "In the Workshop of Time and Tide" first appeared as an appendix to the University of the Philippines Press edition of *Mindoro and Beyond: Twenty-One Stories* (1979). The essay "Moving On: A Filipino in the World" comes from the monograph *Foreign Values and Southeast Asian Scholarship* (Berkeley: University of California, 1973) edited by Joseph Fisher. *Kalutang* was issued by Kalikasan (Manila) in an edition of three hundred copies in 1991. Grateful acknowledgements are due Lourdes Gutierrez for her "Introduction" to *Kalutang*, the whole of which she serialized in *People's Journal* (Manila), a tabloid with a readership of a quarter of a million.

As to *The Father and the Maid*, the six essays that comprise the book were lectures delivered at the University of the Philippines during the period from November 1988 to January 1989. The brief note accompanying the set describes more fully the circumstances surrounding the assignment. In *The Manila Times*, my column "New Windows" carried last July my piece on Ajanta; hence, my thanks to *The Times*.

Grateful acknowledgements also go to *The Virginia Quarterly Review*, where the essay " 'As in Myth, the Signs Were All Over': The Fiction of N.V.M. Gonzalez," by Richard R. Guzman, first appeared. The essay is reprinted here with also the kind permission of the writer.

And, finally, I am most indebted to Professor Oscar V. Campomanes, of the English Department, University of California, Berkeley, for his introduction. To President Emil Q. Javier of the University of the Philippines also go my thanks for his continued sponsorship of creative writing and publishing, and to Director Laura Samson of the University of the Philippines Press and her staff, and June Poticar Dalisay.

All this, however, would be incomplete without mention of the unfailing assistance that my wife Narita Manuel Gonzalez and my entire family have given me; they have made it possible for me, over the years, to consider the thought that, indeed, writing is Ajanta.

I

In the Workshop of Time and Tide

I

*I*s it a tale of the wars?"

"No," was the reply. "(But) I shall tell you something I saw, or rather something (that) I did not see, this afternoon."

This curious exchange from a little-known story by Mariano Pascual perhaps holds a key to an understanding of Philippine literature and, particularly, of the short story in both Pilipino and English. "The Major's Story," as Mr. Pascual's narrative is called, is in Jose Garcia Villa's *Best Philippine Short Stories 1928*, a pioneer anthology of the Philippine practice of this genre, published by *Philippines Free Press*, itself a pioneer in the promotion and development of Filipino letters in general. The Philippines was in those days a frontier, although hardly the badlands, of literature.

The subject and perhaps the rendering of that literature is symbolically given in "The Major's Story." It concerns a party where a number of girls succeed in persuading one of the many guests, in this instance, the Major, to liven up the occasion with some amusing anecdote.

Our Major obliges; he tells the girls about an incident of no paricular significance other than that he could vouch for it. He was on his way home one afternoon, he says, when he spotted a crowd gathering at Colgante Bridge. The crowd, says the Major, included a number of students, two Chinese peddlers, a Spaniard with a little child by his side, some half dozen Yankee sailors, three women in black who had just come from nearby Quiapo Church, and two laborers carrying a pig. Soon enough two policemen appeared, one from the north, the other from the south. It was humanity on a small scale. And what was attracting all that attention? A drowned person? A wreck? Someone doing a stunt in the water below?

"The man beside me began it all," the Major tells the girls, for he has sensed that he cannot hold them in suspense much longer. "He had nothing to do, and to kill time he watched the water as it flowed into the sea. People saw him looking into the water, and, being curious, followed him as people will always do."

As an explanation this is plausible enough. But the thoughtful reader might find the Filipino writer in the episode. For the ceaseless flow of the Pasig is what Filipino literature could be all about. At any point in time, one might ask the question, "What, indeed, does the crowd see?"

Writing some forty years later, Francisco Arcellana offered a synthesis of what our symbolic Pasig, through time and tide, has offered the observer:

> ...Wall Street crashed in 1929. What did that mean for us in 1930? Men jumping out of windows of sky-scrapers....There was a depression in America. The dole, headlines, the hordes of the unemployed. The Philippines became a commonwealth. Japan invaded Asia. There was a civil war in Spain. The International Eucharistic Congress met in Manila. Italy invaded Ethiopia. The Filipino writer was told to leave his ivory tower. He was told to stay there. They read proletarian literature. They wrote proletarian literature. They debated whether to scab or join the picket line. Germany invaded Poland. And the world that we thought was without end began to end.[1]

Eventually, Colgante Bridge was dismantled and junked. The river Pasig, of course, has remained—although perhaps a bit murkier than before. But for as long as it flows there will be stories to tell, and Filipino writers will be writing them for whoever might care to read, wherever that audience might be.

II

IT is not often remembered that the printing press

reached the Philippines as early as the last decade of the sixteenth century and that by 1610, a Filipino printer Tomas Pinpin has produced a primer for Spanish. The first known published poem in Tagalog is said to have appeared in 1605. It took almost a hundred years, however, before *Pasyon ni Hesukristong Panginoon (The Passion of the Lord Jesus Christ)*, by Gaspar Aquino de Belen, was printed. Fifty more years were to pass before the emergence of Jose de la Cruz (1746-1829), better known as Huseng Sisiw, who is credited with having written the first verses that dealt with lay, rather than religious, themes. Finally came Balagtas (1788-1862) and his *Florante at Laura* (1838)

> ...bunga ng pagtatagpo ng tradisyong katutubo at ng impluwensyang banyaga, at karapatdapat tanghaling hiyas ng panulaang Tagalog ng panahon ng kolonyalismong Español.[2]

> (...an outcome of the contact of the native tradition with foreign influences, and [a work which we] must duly esteem as the jewel of Tagalog poetry during the Spanish era.)

There is more to all those years, of course, than "foreign influences." True, the bulk of the formal literature of the period (to distinguish it from the oral) would seem, whether in song or narrative verse, to be mere borrowings from abroad. These were known as the *awit* and *corrido*,[3] the verse forms into which the Filipino poet cast the medieval romances and adventure stories that reached him. The material had spilled over from Europe; in their Filipino containers, they were to remain available for over two hundred years. If early Filipino literature is to be understood, scholars could pay close attention to the awit and corrido.

To the undiscerning, our earliest writers seemed unoriginal, limiting themselves to mere episodes from Spanish chivalric literature and from the Arthurian and Carolingian legends, anecdotes from Portuguese and Italian history latched on at best to incidents from Czech or Persian folklore.

These stories about queens, princesses and princes, knights, dukes, and counts who lived in a wonderful world of romance where the good were always rewarded and the wicked punished, and where God, the Virgin, and the saints communicated frequently with men through angels and heavenly voices, or even came down to help the heroes and heroines in need, captivated the imagination of a people who as yet knew very little of the outside world. These romances provided a temporary release from the harsh realities of existence. They were, however, the only reading matter that the masses could safely enjoy during a period of strict political and literary censorship.[4]

Some fifty of those stories have come down to us, and we have a study by Dr. Damiana Ligon Eugenio of both the verse forms and their European analogues. It is research of this kind that might change the skimpy regard that scholars have held for the national heritage. Summarily dismissed by some writers as embarrassing scraps of an indeterminable literature, the awit and corrido are, in fact, a mirror upon which the culture of their day is truly reflected. An amazing grasp by the Tagalog mind of the fundamentals of literary art is imaged in them, for example, and at the very least this is something to admire.

It was not unusual for the awit and corrido writers to exhibit a disarming humility toward their art, a stance exceeded only by an abiding respect for their audience. The romance, *Salita at Buhay na Pinagdaanan nang Haring Asuero, ni Doña Maria, at ni Juan Pobre sa Bayang Herusalem,* a work of some four hundred and seventy-five quatrains of unknown authorship is perhaps typical. The story, according to Dr. Eugenio, has analogues in the folklore of Italy, France, and Czechoslovakia. The author begins with a formulaic invocation:

Oh God, Lord all Powerful,
Who made and created the whole universe,
Help now my lips and my tongue
To be able to narrate an exemplum.

And all you saints and angels,
Comrades of God the King of Heaven,
Bestow grace on my feeble mind
That I may not err in what I shall say.

Distinguished audience, what can I
Say and declare?
Wherever I look and fix my gaze
I see that all of you are persons of quality.

But be it so, distinguished ones,
I shall begin my story:
If perchance I omit anything,
Let your better judgement supply the deficiency.[5]

This appeal to the better judgment of the "distinguished ones" is what today's entertainers might call "audience participation"; the feature, in any case, placed the versifier in direct contact with his public. What he called the awit required twelve-syllable lines, the corrido eight-syllable ones. He worked with quatrains, observing no particular preferences as to which subjects required the awit or which demanded the corrido form. He might have initially recited his narratives himself; but they were later to see print anyhow, and were in fact soon obtainable at "sidewalk stalls and brought to the remote barrios by itinerant peddlers."[6] Their popularity was undeniable. Translations appeared and these may have helped immeasurably, in the early development of provincial languages like Hiligaynon and Ilocano, for example, to establish the conventions of grammar and rhetoric so necessary for growth.

The tradition of humble authorship did not, of course,

discourage later writers from affixing their signatures to their work. Initials were at times used in the closing quatrain, and with some shrewdness, so as to avoid blunting sentiment for the sake of rhyme. The writer, when torn between veracity to the known turns of a given story and rendering it in some way or other, often gave greater weight to the latter. Thus, in *Proceso*, we find this choice disguised with some naivete in the following subtitle:

> The Life of the Merchant Proceso, and his daughter Maria, in the Kingdom of Hungary, which was derived from a *Cuadro Histórico*, and most laboriously versified by one who is just beginning to write in the common pastime of the Tagalogs.[7]

Francisco Baltazar came from this tradition. Some twelve works have been credited to him; of these only *Florante at Laura*, however, appears to have survived. His predecessor, Huseng Sisiw, is remembered today for *Historia Famosa ni Bernardo Carpio, Doce Pares, Rodrigo de Villa* and others. In Eugenio's study, only fifteen authors, Balagtas and Huseng Sisiw among them, have their writings fairly well authenticated.

There are probably two hundred of these awit and corrido, according to Eugenio. Earlier scholars, notably Epifanio de los Santos, have left us musical scores as well of a few awit samples. Whatever further study might suggest, it seems clear that the roots of the Filipino storyteller's art are in this material.

Song, for one thing, is central to the vocabulary of that art. Read as one of the last scenes of Jose Rizal's recorded life, his valedictory poem, "Mi Ultimo Adios," is not lyrical in quality by mere coincidence.[8] Similarly, before the final curtain in Nick Joaquin's *A Portrait of the Artist as Filipino*, we see

> Bitoy (*speaking exultantly through the sound of bells and music*): October in Manila!...The month when, back in our childhood, the very air turned festive and

the Circus came to town and the old Opera House!

(*The lights die out inside the stage; the sound of bells and music fades off. The ruins stand out distinctly.*)

Oh Paula, Candida—listen to me! By your dust, and by the dust of all the generations, I promise to continue, I promise to persevere!

The jungle may advance, the bombs may fall again—but while I live, you live—and this dear city of our affections shall rise again—if only in my song! To remember and to sing: that is my vocation....[9]

And then, though quite on a different track, we have a confirmation of the same phenomenon from the short-story writers.

"Was she afraid of Labang?" My father had not raised his voice, but the room seemed to resound with it. And again I saw her eyes on the long curving horns and the arm of my brother Leon around her shoulders.

"No, Father, she was not afraid."

"On the way—"

"She looked at the stars, Father. And Manong Leon sang."

"What did he sing?"

" 'Sky Sown with Stars.' She sang with him."[10]

This is from Arguilla's "How My Brother Leon Brought Home a Wife." In J.C. Tuvera's "Ceremony," it appears in somewhat cryptic form but is at the heart of the story:

"I hate it all here," he said. "In this house. And I can't bear to see you leave again."

In a rush the words tumbled from her. "I know," she said. "I know." Then abruptly she bent and touched her lips to his face, in the moment when a spurt of song heaved afresh from the night, and then sobbing she fled swiftly from the room.[11]

III

ART does not copy life but rather illumines it by offering for our enjoyment a semblance of it. And the Filipino story-teller has done well enough in this, as the record of his first hundred and fifty years of apprenticeship shows. Hardly can one fault him for being unengaging; and judging from the awit and corrido that have come down to us, he had in fact an intuitive grasp of his role in society.

Competing and authoritative cultures, such as that which informed the civil regime under Spain and the friarocracy that went with it, were never out of the Filipino artist's way. His experience in those years demonstrates what John Dewey was to insist upon as a characteristic of art, namely, its ability to cope with seemingly obstructive matters. In the practice of the awit and corrido writers, invention and love for the Tagalog language were the tools used to minimize barriers of communication.

Students of the culture, since Father Pedro Chirino's *Relación de las Islas Filipinas* of 1604, have been happily astounded by our capabilities even before the advent of the verse-narrative writers. When the folklore of the world, and particularly that of Europe, became available to the Filipino, the artist in the national community did not appear to require instruction on how to deal with the material; the genius of the race, as it were, took over. We might remember that the long years under Spain were not spectacular for the achievements of that regime in mass education. The authorities undoubtedly saw an ally in the verse-writer, and here commenced the tension in the experience between art and society.

In dismissing the awit and corrido portion of the national heritage, as some have done, and in relegating this to the heap of unsavory by-products of friarocracy, the banal and uninventive in the Filipino character have been exaggerated. This is unfair to the Filipino artistic sensibility since it was after all very much in control, in fact ever since its formative years. Those pious invocations and shy clues to authorship are proofs of this.

They served, to begin with, to dissociate from the art the particulars that story-teller and audience shared and recognized as the nitty-gritty of lived life. They were the story-teller's signals that a narrative was forthcoming and with it a burden of myth and riddle, of fable, a vision of life. And those ritual signatures had a similar, if opposite, purpose: to restore the audience to the lived life, to the actuality that had been disturbed or temporarily abandoned for the story's sake.[12] Audience and story-teller both enjoyed a secret, moreover: that the material really belonged to popular history or lore.

The audience knew that the story-teller's boarding-house reach had come up with something for it to share. Painters experience how the quality of sunlight and the nature of shadows in the country where one has chosen to do one's work—say, Italy—influence the artist's development, his style and methods. With the twelve- or eight-syllable line, and the alliteration and assonance in Tagalog, the awit and corrido writers worked diligently, as it were, with their brush, delighting in simply letting themselves belong to their time and place. They were earlier Fernando Amorsolos, discovering their very own sun-drenched tropical landscape.

The Eugenio study observes that there have been awit and corrido structures that reached from four to more than five thousand lines. Considering the moralistic themes that weighted them down, it was remarkable how they did not disenchant the listener or reader but continued instead to hold and win him. We must go to the archetypal nature of those borrowed stories to understand the phenomenon. For those romances were no mere "histories" or "lives"; they were not topical episodes of adventure. They were, in fact, inherited "deposits" of experience, "banked" answers to life's riddles, motifs of initiations and discoveries. Our awit and corrido writers could not have escaped their mystique; the imagination and its power to put experience in order demanded this understanding of them. To our early loss, we failed to see this intuitive use that our pioneer workers in the field of the imagination made of archetypal images that were as accessible in their day as they have been, of course, in ours.

IV

THOSE archetypes are, as they seem to have always been, informed by that shaping or ordering force. To be aware of this, one has only to recall the tale of the *adarna*—of the sick father who had three sons, and who wanted a magic bird brought to his bedside so that he might become well again.[13] Or consider Balagtas' *Florante at Laura*[14] and its motifs of justice and honor. That political satire has been read into it derives from this archetypal mold that found a particularly revealing parallel in the social reality of Balagtas' time.

John M. Echols has called *Florante at Laura* an "early precursor of the writings of supporters of independence"[15]— an apt description; indeed it was time the writer put his finger on the pulse of the nation. By the middle of the 19th century the most important writings were in Spanish, and "the internationally renowned representative of this period," Echols goes further, "is Jose Rizal, whose novels, *Noli Me Tangere (The Lost Eden)* and *El Filibusterismo (The Subversive)* helped to spark the struggle for independence from Spain...His works were ultimately to help bring about his execution before a Spanish firing squad..."[16] We might recall, in this connection, the last work to come from Rizal's pen, mention of which was made earlier: "Mi Ultimo Adios" (My Last Farewell). It might have been the song of the mythic adarna bird; for such is the way of archetypes.[17]

Such synoptic remarks by disinterested observers like Professor Echols enable us to recognize the direction that Philippine literature has taken. "Writing in Spanish," he tells us in an all-too-brief note on Rizal, "has not reached such heights."[18] We should not indeed forget that, especially towards the last decades of the 19th century, a rising awareness concerning the conditions in the country demanded expression. Spanish, rather than Tagalog, which Huseng Sisiw and Balagtas raised to great levels in their day, was held to be the best medium at this time. Spanish would guarantee access to the ruling elite. Reason and emotion could be appealed to wherever intelligent men might be found. And it is in this context that Rizal's novels acquire a perennial interest. His choice of language was an act of sacrifice; his choice of audience, an expression of idealism. Both sacrifice and idealism were to be reevaluated by another generation, the accruement in irony notwithstanding.

At this point in the national literary history, though, Rizal's artistic act has a special meaning. It was an extension of Balagtas' art and a personal response on the novelist's part to yet another European literary convention. Had Rizal followed Balagtas' lead in the use of Tagalog, he might have been held down by the awit and corrido tradition. The fact is that he turned in another direction. He mapped out a new geography for the literature of his country, indicating the ventures appropriate to the exploration of that territory. Three generations of intellectuals were to go into the terrain, at times flamboyantly flashing their travel documents but only to fail in their capacity as transients or even as protracted sojourners owing to an inability to distinguish, it would seem, between travel and residence, between being merely naturalized and native-born.

Rizal's success derives from his having been a true son of his tradition. Consider his use of the novel form. The awit and corrido, as analogies of the European realistic novel, created a level of rhyme and measure appropriate to a semblance of human experience of archetypal force and blocked off the particular realities of the day. Rizal adopted the paradigm using Spanish and the novel form, the latter having been long employed in Europe. He achieved much the same effect as did the awit and corrido writer in terms of creating a virtual world where ideals could be particularized. It was as if he knew all along that his predecessors in the craft of the narrative had drawn enough from the fables of Europe, and now it was his turn to tell a tale of a Europe transplanted. Here was his necessary subject; both the convention he chose and his tradition required it. The earlier corrido had rendered glosses on the subject of justice; the awit had lyricized over it. Now he would probe for its truth. Convention laid out the tools of realism on a service-tray before him. In place of the twelve-and eight-syllable lines, which were the versifier's bid for immediacy, he would turn to the resources of scene, dialogue, characterization, of persona and tone—devices already pressed into service by Perez Galdos (1843-1920), Dumas (1802-70), Hugo (1802-85), and Flaubert (1821-80).

The popularity of the awit and corrido among the common people and their heavy burden of pious material must have concealed, for Rizal's younger brothers, the profound artistic advance that has been achieved and possibly the creative resources of the national past as well. Rizal, for his part, had the genius not to miss anything. It therefore became necessary for late-comers to make new discoveries. But the complex role in the national culture that Rizal and his work played concealed this purely artistic facet of his legacy, obscuring leads that could help the diligent and the humble. With the advent of the American regime, a perturbed sensibility began to look about, anxious for indications of roots or beginnings, only to stumble into false starts and ludicrous posturings in hopes of pressing the Filipino experience into acceptable forms. In some cases, as we shall later see, the acceptable meant the vendable. Moreover, events moved at much too fast a clip. Before a freshly remembered event was released from memory and could be articulated, a new one thrust itself forward to overwhelm the mind and

14

trample upon the spirit. The short story in both Filipino and English offered relief from this cultural mutilation.

V

THE short story in Pilipino has a less elaborate history than its counterpart in English, although not necessarily a less eventful one. It is unfortunate that the schoolbook trade, like a curse, has encouraged the easy designation of styles and themes and the listing of writers and titles of stories as alternatives to defining the forces that beleaguered the writer and diminished his art. Our account here can not supply what years of diligent critical attention could have provided. We can only sketch in an idea: the dedicated involvement by some writers and the enthusiastic, if chancy, support by certain institutions and groups, so that the appearance of the short story in Pilipino, all told, might be recognized as a milestone in the journey of the Filipino toward artistic expression.

What we call *maikling katha*—a short literary composition—could not be anything but new in the literature, considering its formal beginnings in the awit and corrido tradition. The form derives from the *dagli,* brief sketches that Lope K. Santos and his associates published in *Muling Pagsilang* in the twenties. The *salaysay,* or narration, had already been cultivated as well. It may well be that when the salaysay acquired a thematic thrust the dagli came into being. For one thing, length had lost its appeal; and reading matter that could be sold at the patio of Quiapo Church, alongside votive candles in the shape of hearts and crosses, were now things of the past. No doubt, the Revolution of 1896 and the Philippine-American War, which extended to 1904, were more than sufficient explanations for the change of taste in the images of the lived life. What was sought after was entertainment and instruction for the new age. This was the direction that attracted many a publication or journal of the period, and a typical one was *Ang Mithi.* In a literary competition in 1910 sponsored by this magazine, the story "Elias" by Rosauro Almario won first prize, setting a trend in fiction contests.

In 1920, Cirio Panganiban's "Bunga ng Kasalanan" ("The Fruit of Sin") earned the title "Katha ng Taon," ("Story of the Year") in a contest sponsored by *Taliba.* A.G. Abadilla credits Panganiban with having introduced "plot" (*ang banghay*) to the dagli or salaysay.[19] The "orderly arrangement of events, as a function and feature of the literary composition" (*maayos na pagkakatagni-tagni ng mga nangyari, bilang sangkap at haligi ng katha*) was, according to Abadilla, something of a discovery to this generation.

This was an underestimation of the earlier narrative tradition; for the awit and corrido writers were, of course, no strangers to it. What the new writers did manage was a practical use for plot. Whereas their verse-writing prede-cessors employed plot to mount some tendentious moralizing, the new writers used it to enhance narrative interest, to promote rewards like suspense and surprise. The new writers soon enough slipped into sentimentality, abetted by the lurid prose that had become, alas, the hallmark of popular reading.

And what were their stories about? Abadilla describes their core as follows: "...*ang nakayukayok na kalungkutan, ang inaglahing pag-ibig ng isang mahirap lalo na, ang mga daliring hubogkandila, ang baywang-hantik ng pina-paraluman, at anu-ano pang bunga ng mga kabiglawang pandamdamin at pangkaisipan....*"[20] ("...crushing sorrows, the spurned love of a poor suitor in particular, fingers as shapely as candles, the beloved's waist like that of an ant's, and all sorts of adolescent emotions and thoughts....") Here altogether was an odd way of looking at life, but it was not without admirers.

A readership developed for it in *Liwayway,* a weekly that very early on stood for popular writing in Tagalog. It was in *Liwayway's* pages that the work of the members of the new school almost exclusively appeared. Other weeklies were soon launched, and for the first time the writer as a Filipino (working in what today is called Filipino but which then was essentially the Tagalog of Manila and vicinity) became aware that one could make a living professionally at being a man of letters. Indeed, this was possible through writing fiction as a craftsman in the language of one's own race.

By 1927, the *maikling katha* was prepared for some official accounting. Precisely for this purpose Clodualdo Del Mundo initiated his lists of the best stories published in the magazines. For nine years he stood watch. Writers were observed to compose their work with more care than before, particularly in hopes of making the del Mundo roll of honor, the *Parolang Ginto* (The Golden Lantern).

Another critical observer joined in—Alejandro G. Abadilla, who, earlier on, had earned a reputation for his poetry. Inaugurated in 1932, Abadilla's *Talaang Bughaw* (The Blue List) exerted pressure on contributors to both popular weeklies and college publications alike. Here was a critic who was keen on craft and willing to keep running skirmishes over the years with those writers gleefully unconcerned with technique.

The practitioners of the maikling katha had much to thank the Abadilla and del Mundo leadership for. In due course, however, the Tagalog scene became polarized. A sharp division between *Liwayway* writers—who now became the old school—and the young blood was all too discernible by 1935, the year of the participation of the academy in the national literary dialogue. For it was then that the National Teachers College offered the use of its facilities for seminars and debates on Tagalog literary issues. The dialogue tended toward dismantling what appeared to be a strong literary fort manned by members of the *Liwayway* camp and their supporters from the staff of similarly minded magazines. The new writers, unable to publish readily in the popular press, were not without ingenuity and enterprise. In the following year appeared the first anthology of the short story in

Tagalog, *Mga Kuwentong Ginto (Golden Tales)*, edited by A.G. Abadilla and C. del Mundo.[21]

The collection contained twenty stories and covered the period from 1925 to 1935. Here the Pilipino term for "short story" seems to have seen print for the first time. The anthologists defined the form as best they could. Quite apart from the many stories that are already short, they observed, the maikling katha are those that are a class by themselves owing to the attentive regard on the part of their authors for meaning and structure. Each story in *Mga Kuwentong Ginto* could come close, in the estimation of the editors, to what might be called the *sining ng maikling katha* (the art of the short story).

All this had a beneficial effect, as reflected in the work by the new writers, many of them still college undergraduates. And from here on, the short story in Pilipino became an open arena for protracted contest between two groups, invariably the old and the young. To the first belonged those committed to the standards set by *Liwayway* and like publications whose survival meant their catering to a large but undiscriminating audience. The writers of the second group had no such loyalties and made no concessions to popular taste. They felt free to experiment with form and to leave fresh ideas on it. The publication of *50 Kuwentong Ginto ng 50 Batikang Kuwentista (Fifty Golden Stories by Fifty Master Story-tellers)* edited by Pedrito Reyes[22] had the effect of placing the innovators in a most advantageous position.

The battle lines seem to have been clearly drawn now although larger issues, then unidentified, began to appear. The *Liwayway* school, it will be recalled, did not particularly recognize a literary past. But it did identify enough with the romantic sentiments that, in the work of the awit and corrido writers, had won popular approval. While dutifully extolling Huseng Sisiw and Balagtas, the *Liwayway* school also accommodated itself to the stock situations and cliche ideas that the reading public sought. Attempts at new modes and the search for new directions were readily discouraged. Rather than raise the level of the narrative form in any serious way, the *Liwayway* school settled for professionalism in the business of producing popular literature, regarding this as a virtuous gesture suited to the peculiarities of the pursuit of letters in a country without its own sources of newsprint and other paper products.

Its writers rode high on the assets that have accrued to the language through its formal use in the folklore, gains achieved by those chapbooks of the church-patio and through *sari-sari* store level of distribution. Instead of being sold side by side with votive offerings and from counters with candy jars and sugar-and-peanut cakes, the work of the *Liwayway* writer would now reach the reader by courtesy of a modern delivery service. Printing empires were in the making. What the younger writers could not accept, obviously, was to see literary imagination become a tool of wealth and trade. This sentiment was not, however, easily expressed. While mindful of the service that the popular magazines were providing by spreading the idiom to distant reaches of the archipelago, the younger writers felt that their elders were doing Philippine culture a disservice. In their evolving concept of the theory and practice of the short story, a growing conflict between practicality and idealism began to be evident.

But the members of the new group were caught up in mundane problems themselves, and the importance of their stand against commercialization was not infrequently obscured by their employment in the very publishing empires that had routed earlier idealisms. The universities and colleges were shortly to provide the country new talent to replace that which by force of circumstances had been weaned away from literature. In this respect the progress of the writers in Tagalog paralleled that of their contemporaries who, using the English language and enjoying the sanctuary of the university, were already writing memorable short stories.

VI

THE Filipino short story in English is a reaction against the commercialization of the Filipino's intuitive grasp of his cultural history. We have seen how the awit and corrido writers reached out to Europe and succeeded in keeping a national community stocked with virtual images of life for its edification. When the Filipino mind, owing to an accident of history, accommodated itself to this unique form of the narrative called the modern short story, a similar performance had to be produced by the shaping imagination. This began in the late twenties and early thirties, about the same time that writers in Tagalog were themselves becoming disturbed over the way the literary tradition in the native language was being used. This confluence of awareness by both groups of writers was no coincidence. There was in the maturing Filipino spirit a need for fuller growth.

Although too easy a choice as a common language for peoples otherwise isolated within their vernaculars, English would be acceptable enough as a tool for growth. Its history and tradition, its metaphysics and rhetoric, more than sufficed to serve as serious barriers to the average learner. And this, too, was endurable. As in several countries that were later to be called the Third World,[23] English would serve as the language of government. But what was one to make out of those elements amongst the governed that dared to give artistic expression to their thoughts and sentiments in a school-learned language? Could this be anything but foolhardiness?[24]

At this point, Rizal's adoption of Spanish was simply too much a matter of consciousness in the Filipino. Spanish was no *wikang sinuso* to Rizal. It was not an idiom drawn, as the Tagalog would say, from Mother's breast. And Rizal had to borrow not only a language but a literary form as well—adding debt upon heavy debt. He did clear the account, though, at an all-too-punitive interest rate. The writers that were to come, then, after Rizal's martyrdom in 1896, could not quite escape his example. By the time the learning of the English language moved from the improvised classrooms of the Thomasites to Gabaldon-style schoolhouses and, finally by the early twenties, to the University of the Philippines and elsewhere, Rizal's example had become transformed as a challenge. Another generation of inheritors of that restless and durable artistic sensibility in the race had emerged.

Some initial efforts at self-identification cannot be recalled without embarrassment. In 1912, Fernando Maramag wondered, for example, if some critic might be found who would tell the nation whether it would be "susceptible to the imaginings of a native Tennyson."[25] The public would thus be "capable of receiving a poet's message with the uplifting sympathy that reaches the divine in man." Besides being a working newspaperman, Maramag was a practicing poet on the scene. Well enough heard was his call for the man of the hour who would tell the nation "whether the ideals and aspirations of the race" could find full expression in the newly learned language. Maramag stipulated, however, that such ideals must remain "distinctly" native.[26]

Thirteen years later, Jorge Bocobo put the national literary community on the alert. (And this has been the condition of the national scene ever since.) "In what language shall this Filipino literature be written?" Bocobo asked. Already the awit and corrido tradition seemed to have been forgotten. Nor had oral literature been able to win its due. A fresh elitism, as when *ilustrado* and *cacique* tastes prevailed, was in the air.

But like Maramag and other intellectuals of the period, Bocobo had not escaped the national inheritance of artistic sensibility. Besides writing plays, he launched a movement to preserve the national heritage in dance and song although his concerns continued to dally with writing. "Less and less will it be in Spanish, and more and more in English." Yet all that would be temporary: eventually "the great Filipino novel...will not be written in English; it will be in one of the Filipino languages."

However that would be, the next decade found a more unequivocal advocate for English in Salvador P. Lopez, who was confident that the literature would "draw increasing sustenance through the old roots that first grew there [the University of the Philippines campus] twenty-five years ago..." The publishers of *Philippines Free Press* were to issue, in a couple of years, Jose Garcia Villa's pioneering selection of the best short stories in English, from a crop of nearly six hundred that particular year. The *Free Press* was to say, without so much as a smile, that behind its effort to provide support for Filipino writing in English was,

> apart from self-interest, [the desire] to develop a school of Filipino short story writers or authors, partly with a view to the development of some literary genius who might make a name for himself in the United States...[27]

What this meant was that the choice of English—that is, if the writer did have a choice—essentially opened up for him an opportunity that could be overlooked only out of sheer boorishness. Compared to the situation in which Rizal's artistic sensibility achieved its successes, this one was less ideal although it had the advantage of being apolitical; and such illusions and realities as it implied had to be recognized for what they were.

Now becoming attractive as a personal gesture of considerable public value was the act of writing itself, a national ideal that found expression in the Commonwealth constitution, particularly in the provision that defined the role of the state as a patron of arts and letters. Although literature did not count as a learned profession, say, like the law, its practitioners had to congregate in Manila where facilities for publishing were available. Besides the *Free Press*, other magazines and journals took special interest in developing, in particular, the short story—the *Graphic, Philippine Magazine,* and weekend supplements to the *Manila Tribune* and *Philippines Herald,* to name the principal ones. A new anthology had followed Villa's; this one was edited by O.O. Sta. Romana, then a senior at the University of Santo Tomas who led, in developing an awareness of posterity, a growing corps of short story writers out of university classrooms and into editors' cubicles and press rooms as fledgling journalists. A civic-minded Philippine Book Guild issued titles by Villa, Manuel E. Arguilla, Arturo B. Rotor; the University of the Philippines student literary annual, not inappropriately named *The Literary Apprentice,* founded years back, now obtained fresh money from the university president's entertainment budget.[28] The thirties were ending; the time had come to make good the state's promise of patronage. Hence the First Commonwealth Literary Awards in 1940.

The stories of Manuel E. Arguilla (who, with his collection, *How My Brother Leon Brought Home a Wife and Other Stories,* won the year's Commonwealth Prize for the Short Story in English)[29] were not typical of the work of the period; nor were those by Arturo B. Rotor.[30] But the high quality of their work came to be regarded as pledges for still more outstanding writing to come and as a standard that could be achieved by the rank and file through a formal study of the form. Indeed, later writers were to pursue studies abroad and test themselves there. Let it be noted, though, that the short story writers in Tagalog moved on as well although not necessarily ahead, and more or less on an independent course. At the time of the Japanese Occupation, though, several short story writers in English tried writing in Tagalog (it would be several years still before the language would be officially called Pilipino); and the experiment, apart from having been required by the exigencies of the war, received considerable welcome.[31]

Largely understood, if hardly admitted or discussed, was the lesson that the two writing groups were each learning from the other. The writer in Tagalog could see what sheer book-learning and formal, if self-conscious, techniques could accomplish; the writer in English saw how inspiration, derived from being able to reach an audience beyond the university campus, could generate material closer to actuality. These were secret lessons, as it were, grasped in the privacy of the artistic conscience. It was becoming possible, in any case, to document Philippine life through the short story—borrowed ostensibly from Edgar Allan Poe, O. Henry and Wilbur Daniel Steele. The Filipino imagination, however, did not seem comfortable with the styles that these writers represent; it favored plotlessness and its ultimate form in the so-called "slice of life."[32] This preference was sustained when soon after, the early stories of Ernest Hemingway and William Saroyan, along with those of Sherwood Anderson, began to exert a strong influence on the Filipino writer's sense of literary structure and his feel for language. Especially for the writers who chose English as their medium, persistence and discipline paid off.

This success could have been more spectacular had Filipinos been familiar at this time with relevant literary experiences in neighboring countries. The Philippine scene had become too much a client of the American cultural establishment in those years before World War II; the Filipino intellectual was thus deprived of the instruction that cultures close by, in Southeast Asia and South Asia, could offer.

T. Inglis Moore, who had been a lecturer at the University of the Philippines, was to remark in 1947 how similar to that of his native Australia the experience in the Philippines was in regard to the use of the English language for literary expression. This was, of course, not too appropriate a comparison. After all, Australia had had as an English colony her original stock of native-born speakers of the language. But the outback, which had become a rich source of material for Australian writing, had its counterpart in the Philippines. T. Inglis Moore felt the intensifying creativity in the air: the Philippines would soon have its own Henry Lawsons and Henry Handel Richardsons. He was of course to reconsider his enthusiasm when, at a latter date, he wrote:

> When a colonial people has already enjoyed a traditional culture of its own, the conflict between this and the conquering culture of an alien people is comparatively clear-cut. This can be seen in the Philippines after 1898 when the new Anglo-Saxon culture of the American conqueror was imposed upon the Spanish-Filipino one established during the centuries of Spanish rule, and the Filipino then struggled to achieve mental independence from colonialism by the creation of a national literature. While political freedom has been won, the cultural struggle still goes on. This is the constant theme of the Filipino literary critics.[33]

It is, in fact, the preoccupation of all Third World criticism as well. A complementary lesson could have been offered by Indo-Anglian literature, too. The careers of Tagore and Sri Aurobindo, Mulk Raj Anand, R.K. Narayan and Raja Rao were to be truly relevant to the Filipino shortly. On occasion, then as now, and like Philippine writing in English, Indo-Anglian writing would in fact be required by nationalists to stoke the fires of an idealism that could cause writers to dream and write in their native tongues.

What urged the Filipino writer, perhaps happy enough in his insularity, to persevere in his craft? What drove him to write in English as much as· he did? He knew that while he could publish his stories in magazines and journals, getting a book out was an entirely different matter. In the latter case, the project would be

> ...delayed for months, to be squeezed in quickly by the press between run-offs of comic books and political broadsides....[34]

Why do his best producing copy for the

> ...Sunday supplements which, by Wednesday, may become torches for burning out nests of termites?[35]

The Indo-Anglian writer also experiences all that and much more; what sees him through is, according to C.D. Narasimhaiah, an "inwardness," a familiarity that spills over into total control of the received language.[36] And given that, what pushes the Indo-Anglian writer yet further on? The promise of audiences? Or

> ...the challenge of particular dispositions and suscepti-
> bilities which can only respond to the possibilities of
> a medium—in its presence will he feel called upon to
> give shape and substance to the unwrought urn, the
> unheard melody and, generally, give airy nothing a
> local habitation and a name.[37]

All this notwithstanding, the artist quite simply obeys, in Narasimhaiah's view, "his own inner law."

Among Filipino writers that "inner law" demanded, in addition to a surrender to inwardness, an acceptance of historical circumstances and participation as a social being through self-fulfillment. With English, there was a considerable tradition that he could turn to. In the most practical terms, this meant working with words, which in turn meant working with authoritative dictionaries. This was an advantage that even the writer working in Tagalog did not have. It would be years, through the efforts of an Australian priest who worked all by himself during the Japanese Occupation, before a fairly substantial English-Tagalog dictionary would appear.[38]

Another factor worked in favor of the Filipino writer in English, one which offset his isolation from the larger world of international letters and transcultural issues. This was the not inconsiderable critical dialogue on the scene. The climate for it appeared to be right. Particularly in the fifties and sixties, literary criticism attained a vigorous, self-questioning voice. Such vapid topics as "Can writing be taught?" and "Where's the Great Filipino Novel?" were thin disguises for insights into the direction the writers were going. The Abadilla and Del Mundo team was preoccupied with the same issues as their brethren working in English, but their scene did not offer the kind of excitement that the writers in the school-learned language found tending their literary potted plants regularly provided with water drawn from the critical fountains of America and England.

By the late sixties, the high hopes of the *Free Press* had been fairly well forgotten, especially as the beginnings of a trade publishing in English surfaced in Manila. Central to the entire literary activity by now was the need for more reader support: an accounting had to be made as to whom the Filipino writer could reach, and especially in his own country. Leonard Casper, who watched the progress that was being achieved and, in 1962, published *Modern Philippine Short Stories*,[39] had to sound a warning. It seemed apparent to him that for the Filipino writer in English "to write honestly *about* his people, he must risk not writing *for* them."[40]

Ironic enough as this appears, it cannot be denied that before the bar of literature the Filipino short story writer in English was nonetheless acquitting himself quite well. Commenting on Casper's anthology, Donald Keene wrote:

> Whatever course Philippine literature may take, we are certainly fortunate that there are now Filipinos who can speak to us beautifully in our own language, without risking the terrible hazards of translation....The collection as a whole is of even more importance than the individual excellences. It is an admirable testimony to the emergence of another important branch of English literature.[41]

What was happening then was that while the Filipino writer in English might not be succeeding in getting to his people, from out of his tussles with a language not his own and with a form relatively new in his culture, he was being counted as a contributor to world literature. For perhaps the Filipino short story writer in English was beginning to be the most instructive and unbiased observer of Philippine life, not to say the most accessible one as well. The difficulties of translation and the built-in intramurals among writers in Pilipino—on the issue between purism and contemporary idiom, for example—have cost the latter much time and energy. The Filipino writer in English was spared this dissipation when history offered him a language and a literary tradition. What he had to mind was an inwardness for both. He might have told off his detractors, as Kamala Das did, defining a premise for the survival, if not the continued good health, of Indo-Anglian writing:

> I am Indian, very brown, born in Malabar, I
> speak three languages, write in two, dream in one.
> Don't write in English,
>   they said,
> English is not your mother tongue. Why not leave
> Me alone, critics, friends, visiting cousin,
> Everyone of you, why not let me speak in
> Any language I like? The language I speak
> Becomes mine...
>   It voices my joys, my longings,
> My hopes, and it is useful to me as cawing
> Is to the crows or roaring to lions, it
> Is human speech, the speech of a mind that is
> Here and not there, a mind that sees and hears and
> Is aware....[42]

Beyond the level of words, for that matter, the Filipino short story writer in English was voicing similar thoughts of his own. We realize this when we understand the kinds of statements that fiction, and particularly the short story, do make. Literary conventions have vocabularies of their own, and, of course, a grammar and a rhetoric that the writer puts at his disposal. It may well be that the Filipino writer was not quite aware of this then; and this is probably fortunate, since more self-consciousness could have destroyed him.

Although introduced as an exciting discovery in *Story*, Manuel E. Arguilla led the group of writers presented to an international audience in the Casper collection. Now, they could speak beyond the borders of their country. The collection included A.B. Rotor, Francisco Arcellana, Edith Tiempo and many others. More collections by other editors followed. Casper himself supplemented his work in 1962 with *New Writing from the Philippines*.[43] A more than modest beginning in terms of international notice had been accomplished. The record to date is, in fact, rather impressive for an art that could be regarded by some as a country cousin to Maupassant and Chekhov. The gods have been rather generous.

VII

THE brevity of the short story is its essential disguise. This feature enables it to appear almost inconspicuous and to work its other disarming charms on the reader much in the same way the earlier Filipino verse-makers rendered their romances, opening their world of make-believe in the mode of the day. Instead of drawing from the lore of Europe, the story writer today had sought the lore of the modern world, and, working within the limits of the form, he has raised questions about his past and future, as Nick Joaquin has done, or about the ways of tradition as Manuel Arguilla and others have. He had defined certain states of the human condition brought on by war and exile, as in the work of Bienvenido N. Santos in *You Lovely People*,[44] class and status are probed with scalpel-sharp felicity as in the stories of Aida Rivera Ford[45] and Gilda Cordero-Fernando.[46] Examples of particular triumphs are too numerous to mention; suffice it to say that the sharpness of its thrust, the revelation of character usually required by the form, or the equally necessary discovery of some idiosyncracy of human life, the focus on an image that becomes an idea objectified...these and other skills that the short story brings off, and memorably, have come under the Filipino short story writer's control. Now, having achieved that, he has favored the form, cherishing it in fact above others—the novel and the play, for example—to a point where the muses that preside hereabouts could well be truly jealous.

And the short story has managed to be left alone. Over the years its writers in the Philippines have not allowed it to be commercialized. This trend has also been observed in the American short story. Its writers have been

> ....left pretty much to themselves, freed from any expectations and preconceptions but their own as they begin to write. It is true that the old-fashioned commodity producers, of the sort who crowded the pages of so many large-circulation magazines now defunct, would be having a hard time of it had they not shrewdly followed their some-time readers into the newer technologies. But the short story in America at the present time, insofar as one may generalize, thrives in its apparent neglect, perhaps even because of it.[47]

The Filipino short story writer in English, and indeed the new generation of writers in Pilipino as well, know this phenomenon from having to live with it. Growth has resulted from the tradesman's indifference and the durability of the artist's sensibility. For what preoccupations could possibly wear that down?

Through good times and bad, through the symbolic floods, through hours of high and low tide at the river Pasig, this sensibility has not denied itself the wonder of expression. There has been no moment in the national experience when the bridge over the Pasig was without curious people looking at the water.

We must recognize their presence unequivocally. For Art is often surrounded by twilight-cool indifference. It is not difficult for a writer to feel at times that the society he serves is a ward of "catatonic patients who make sure only at the end of their trance that nothing escapes them."[48] In the

Philippine experience, that trance has been intermittently broken: the artist does get heard. In any case, "it may not be entirely senseless," as Max Horkheimer reminds us, "to continue speaking a language that is not easily understood."[49]

1976.

Notes

1. Francisco Arcellana, "Period of Emergence: The Short Story," *Brown Heritage: Essays on Philippine Cultural Tradition and Literature*, ed. Antonio Manuud (Quezon City: Ateneo de Manila University Press, 1967), pp. 606-07.
2. "Kasaysayan ng Tulang Tagalog," *Landasin sa Panulaang Tagalog* (Quezon City: Pamana ng Panitikang Pilipino, n.d.), p. 1.
3. Many writers use the plural forms, Anglicizing the terms accordingly. *Awit* is Tagalog for "song"; *corrido* is believed to have derived from "ocurrido," meaning "event or happening." It is Tagalog that was used for the narrative verse derived from the European legends and their adaptations.
4. Damiana Ligon Eugenio, *Awit and Korrido: A Study of Fifty Philippine Metrical Romances in Relation to Their Sources and Analogues*, Ph.D. Diss. University of California, Los Angeles, 1965.
5. *Ibid.*, pp. 395-96.
6. *Ibid.*, pp. 8-9.
7. *Ibid.*, p. 10.
8. For a translation, see Nick Joaquin, *Prose and Poems* (Manila: Alberto S. Florentino, 1963), pp. 191-93.
9. Nick Joaquin, *Portrait of the Artist as Filipino* (Manila: Alberto S. Florentino, 1966).
10. Manuel E. Arguilla, "How My Brother Leon Brought Home a Wife," *Modern Philippine Short Stories* (Albuquerque: University of New Mexico Press, 1962), pp. 59-67.
11. J. C. Tuvera, "Ceremony," from *Fifty Great Oriental Stories*, ed. Gene Z. Hanrahan (New York: Bantam Books 1965), pp. 399-407.
12. See J.R. Rayfield, "What is a Story?" *Journal of the American Anthropological Association*, 74:5 (October 1972), pp. 1085-1106.
13. Eugenio, pp. 372-94.
14. *Ibid.*, pp. 438-47.
15. John M. Echols, *Literature of Southeast Asia* (New York: rpt.

Educational Resources/Asia Literature Program, The Asia Society, n.d.), p. 4.

16. *Ibid.*

17. N.V.M. Gonzalez, "Rizal and Poetic Myth," *Literature and Society* (Manila: Florentino, 1964), pp. 32-54.

18. Echols, *op. cit.,* p. 4.

19. A.G. Abadilla, F.B. Sebastian, and A.D.G. Mariano, *Ang Maikling Kathang Tagalog* (Quezon City: Bedes' Publishing, 1954), p. 5.

20. *Ibid.,* p. 11.

21. Manila: Cavite Publishing Co., 1936.

22. Manila: Ramon Roces Publications, 1939.

23. N.V.M. Gonzalez, "Imagination and the Literature of Emerging Nations," *Solidarity*, IX:5, pp. 31-40, and "Holding the Rainbow," *Manila Review*, 1:3, pp. 59-68.

24. N.V.M. Gonzalez, "The Filipino and the Novel," *Fiction in Several Languages*, ed. Henri Peyre (Boston: Beacon Press, 1968), pp. 19-29.

25. *Loc. cit.*

26. *Loc. cit.*

27. *Loc. cit.*

28. Elmer Ordoñez, "Remembered by the Clowns," *Literary Apprentice*, XX:2 (October 1956). p. 58.

29. Manila: Philippine Writers Guild, 1940.

30. Manila: Philippine Writers Guild, 1937.

31. Under the auspices of the Manila Shinbunsya, *Liwayway* editors published the anthology of Tagalog short stories *Ang 25 Pinakamabuting Maikling Kathang Pilipino ng 1943* (Manila: 1944).

32. Robert Scholes and Robert Kellogg, *The Nature of Narrative* (New York: Oxford, 1966), p. 13.

33. T. Inglis Moore, *Social Patterns in Australian Literature* (Berkeley: University of California Press, 1971), p. 93.

34. Leonard Casper, *Modern Philippine Short Stories* (Albuquerque, New Mexico: University of New Mexico Press, 1962), p. xvii.

35. *Ibid.*

36. N.V.M. Gonzalez, "Holding the Rainbow," *Manila Review*, 1:3, pp. 59-68.

37. C.D. Narasimhaiah, *The Swan and the Eagle* (Simla: Institute of Advanced Study, 1968), p. 11.

38. Leo James English, C.Ss.R., *English-Tagalog Dictionary* (Manila: Department of Education, R.P., 1965). Printed in Australia under the auspices of the Australian Government, this work covered

"more material" than did a similar one undertaken by the Philippine Institute of National Language. The Australian Government, through an arrangement under the Colombo Plan, donated the entire edition of 80,000 copies to the Philippine Government as a "practical token of cooperation" between the two countries.

39. Casper, *op.cit.*
40. *Ibid.*, p. xviii.
41. Donald Keene, "Native Voices in a Foreign Tongue," *Saturday Review of Literature*, October 6, 1962, p. 44.
42. Narasimhaiah, *op.cit.*, p. 13.
43. Syracuse, New York: Syracuse University Press, 1966.
44. Manila: Benipayo, 1955.
45. *Now and at the Hour* (Manila: Benipayo, 1957).
46. *The Butcher, the Baker and the Candlestick-maker* (Manila: Benipayo, 1962).
47. William Abrahams, *Prize Stories 1972: The O. Henry Awards* (New York: Doubleday, 1972, pp. xi-xii.
48. Max Horkheimer, *Critical Theory* (New York: Herder & Herder, 1972), p. 290.
49. *Ibid.*

II

Kalutang:
A Filipino in the World

To the memory of
A.V.H. Hartendorp,
Bienvenido Gonzalez,
Cristino Jamias
and
Jose Luna Castro

Foreword

"All we do as writers is carve away at the mountain of reality and then pass on the pick and shovel to the next in line," the Filipino International Writer-in-Residence at the University of the Philippines sums up a lifetime of writing and teaching.

We are sitting across each other over a *kare-kare* lunch at the Asin Institute of Tourism coffee shop—the professor and the student communing after many, many years of separation, totally unmindful of the noonday chatter around us.

He used to make short story writing seem like child's play in the days when the English Department was part of the College of Liberal Arts, until we agonized over our first paragraph.

Even then, N.V.M. (Nestor Vicente Madali) Gonzalez, he with the ubiquitous pipe in hand, stood tall among his students.

Four waves of English majors sorely missed him when he left U.P. Diliman to accept an invitation to teach at the University of California at Sta. Barbara and, later, at California State University, Hayward. But discover him they did by reading and rereading his short stories and novels, *Seven Hills Away, Children of the Ash-Covered Loam*, and *The Bamboo Dancers*, among others.

Now a new generation of citified students are finding in N.V.M.'s stories the same freshness and robustness of spirit that Pura Santillan Castrence described in her introduction to *Seven Hills Away*, a collection of twelve tales on the Filipino farmer set in the backwoods of Mindoro.

"The stories are simple—simple to the extent of being elemental; they are natural, with the naturalness of peasant folk, veracious because they are sincere, earnest and un-sophisticated.

"One feels that the stories err on the side of under-statement most of the time and silently reproaches the author for leaving so much untold.

"Yet," Castrence continues, "N.V.M. Gonzalez, among our writers, has preserved in beautiful English the Filipino soul."

Even with his mastery of the borrowed language, N.V.M. Gonzalez admits that things started to go wrong in the Philippine experience "when we adopted English as a national language."

He admits wrestling with a double inferiority as he trudged with *maleta* in hand from the barrio in the direction of the city—an inferiority stemming from the adoption of English as the medium of instruction in the public school system and the economic and political advantages of his urbanized peers.

N.V.M.'s autobiography, *Kalutang: A Filipino in the World*, which *Sunday PJ* serialized, is a personal awakening of a Filipino who journeys from the barrio to the city, to Hayward and beyond.

The writer provides the reader with a key to under-standing the Philippines—a process which begins in the realization that it is one nation made up of three countries.

"Manila is the capital of the first country, which is The City. The second country, The Barrio, has a capital known by many names: Aplaya, Bondok, Wawa—whatever. All these names do not celebrate a dubious piety—San Felipe, San Roque, etc.—but somehow honor the very life of the land, calling Nature, as it were, by its true name.

"The third country, The Mountain, by its very nature needs no capital, or center, although it shares with The Barrio a calculated distance from The City."

He has shaken off history's despotism by going through a three-staged development process which finds the writer initially attempting to assimilate the "occupying (colonizing) culture, experiencing withdrawal and a search for identity" in the second stage, and seeking out our own people for instruction and inspiration, joining our talents with their aspirations, in the final phase.

At 74, the professor, now retired from California State University, Hayward, and with still nine months to wind up his residency contract, he follows a rigid self-imposed work schedule that is likely to wear out a much younger person.

"A short novel, *KainginCountry*, is in its final draft and there is a sheaf of poems, *A Wanderer Through the Night of the World*, which I brought out this morning to work on," N.V.M. says.

"On deck is *Mother the Provider*, a collection of stories, and *The Father and the Maid*, a compilation of six lectures.[1]

"The New Day edition of *Mindoro and Beyond* [2] has just come out.

"You must like what you do to have one hundred percent support from the people around you. Organize yourself so that your writing becomes the center of your life and everything else is peripheral."

Apparently his family—wife Narita, an environmentalist, children Father Nim, S.J., Selma, Lakshmi, and Mike—have stood by him "through deprivation and comfort."

At a U.P Tinta-sponsored[3] forum on career options for English majors, he nudges aspiring writers to stretch the limits of their creativity.

"Employers will grab you. Your exposure to world literature has given you an edge over other job-seekers. You have ISI—I for imagination, S for sensitivity, and I for integrity. I know you will not sell out.

"Will you get a chance to go to India?" he asks out of the blue.

"If you do nothing else, go to Bombay and fly out to

---

1 Quezon City: University of the Philippines Press, 1990. These are lectures delivered at the U.P. under the sponsorship of the Likhaan: Sentro ng Makathaing Pagsulat (Creative Writing Center).

2 Originally published by the U.P. Press in 1979.

3 Tinta is a U.P. student organization of English majors.

Ajanta. There you will find several caves that had been carved out of the sandstone mountain—one is under a waterfall!—by Buddhist monks more than two thousand years ago and discovered in 1815, when a hunter saw a tiger disappear into its inner recesses.

"Opposite is Ellora, where Hindu monks had built huge statues of marble."

Like these monks of ancient India, writers add to and substract from reality, and pass on the pick and shovel to the next in line.

LOURDES GUTIERREZ[*]

---

[*] Lourdes Gutierrez, managing editor of *People's Journal*, introduced *Kalutang* to its readers with this essay, originally entitled "Preserver of Our Soul." Used with permission.—*Publisher*

I

*I*t is said that among the Hanunoos the body and the soul are not readily separated.

William Golding has written about how such separation feels in this jet age. He does not paint a very happy picture of our efforts to keep the soul from detaching itself from the body and wandering away. There is a lust in the soul to go gallivanting about; the body is much more easily held in check.

Am awake, dammit, or rather body is awake, soul two thousand miles behind, passing through Nashville, Tennessee, shall never be whole again, body mouldering in the jet, soul marching on towards Denver. Time? Bump, rumble, rumble, lights, lights! Los Angeles. Time? Enter Belshazzar's Hall. Body finds hall moving slowly, but they can't fool body.

Body knows the movement is the world turning to catch up. More halls, enough for whole dynasties of Belshazzars.[1]

But the body is not too easily fooled. Nor is it even misled or ill-directed.

I have lived with the Hanunóos; I grew up among them. I have watched them walk down the jungle trail, interminably making song with two wooden sticks. The song helps the soul know where the body is.

Through stretches of fern and embankments of vine, across clearings and second growth, the music travels. Its maker pauses, looking idly up at the sky or swatting a stubborn leech off his leg.

The beating of the sticks changes the rhythm from slow to fast; it may even dissolve altogether into silence, coming through again, in a lilting, graceful theme or as a trembling against the stillness of sun-mottled leaves. And then there is a scuffing of dry twigs or the crunch of tree bark.

For our Hanunóo is once more on the move, now with body and soul together.

What follows is an account of my own journey, with my own two wooden sticks. At first I did not know where I was going. Eventually, I did and I continued on, assured not only of the direction I was taking but also of the presence of a self entire.

II

These tales have given me great deal of pleasure and edification. The richness of color and folklore made them especially interesting to me.

THUS wrote Edgar Snow about some of my earliest stories. Only a few years earlier, he had edited an anthology of modern Chinese stories. His collection introduced me to Lu Xun and the possibilities of the short story.

Today, given twenty anthologies of short stories from over the world, you might find one piece, perhaps, of Lu Xun's. But this was not so in the late forties, when I was searching the literature. When I finally came across Lu Xun, I felt I had found a writer whose way of dealing with scenes and people I might profitably study. His scenes and people were, though not familiar, close enough to me.

You might ask: How Chinese was your environment? Answer: All but a few towns in the Philippines have at least one functioning Chinese merchant (although no one would boast of this.)

My reading as a writer had been confined till then to English and American authors. There were no others to be had, quite literally. I had escaped formal education and, therefore, had been liberated from George Eliot.[2] But to survive as a freelance writer—one is tempted to add "struggling," but the rhetoric would falsify rather than make the truth more credible—I had to like Saki and Dorothy Parker.

Numerous other writers of similar sophistication had been thrust on me as models by no less than the well-intentioned magazine editor to whose literary pages I hoped to contribute. The implication was that I should be as glib, clever, and idiomatic as those sensitive writers. I have no doubt that this editor must have acquired a great deal of his literary taste from the Christian Brothers, whose genuine interests in the education of youth can only be matched, perhaps, by the Jesuits.

This is not a religious fact but a sociological one, and not only verifiable in the Philippines. The Christian Brothers were carriers of culture in Southeast Asia and their equally generous counterparts were among the ten percent of the North American religious which, in 1960, had been invited to work the missions in Latin America.[3]

This is not a digression; the point is that an imagination, a sensibility, that emerges out of a Third World environment, must fend for itself, for it is easy prey to the rabid charity of other worlds.

To overlook the examples set by my clever literary models was impossible. I told myself, "You've already bought your first pair of leather shoes from the proceeds of a poem. What could be a better omen! How long ago was it when you took weekly trips to the municipal post office, twelve kilometers from the barrio where you lived, to post—and then get back in two weeks—your manuscripts? Homing pigeons, your father used to say of them. But he was unable to discourage your efforts. Indeed, that was long ago. And now you have to be sharp and lively—and read *Chrome Yellow* and even *Antic Hay*."

Fortunately, my efforts were somewhat rewarded. Borrowing carfare from my brother, who earned his pin money shining shoes in the street, I attended the first Commonwealth Literary Contest Awards of 1939 to receive a five-hundred peso check from President Manuel L. Quezon himself.

Besides earning this munificence, *The Winds of April* drew a kind notice in *Asia Magazine* from Elsie Weil. The war came between that work and *Seven Hills Away*, the collection of stories about Mindoro that Alan Swallow published in Denver. It is interesting to recall today that Swallow thought these stories to be folklore, although I wrote them, I felt, as factual renderings of an environment I knew.

Could it be, then, that at that time our life was sheer folklore? The thought is delightfully frightening. In any case, it was those stories that had moved Edgar Snow to write me, acknowledging warmly the copy of the book I had sent him. I could not take his words casually. The year was 1947.

III

THOSE stories were mere "tales." Although they earned me a year's study at Stanford, they were not what my mentors cared to be bothered with. At that time they were deep into the theory and practice of what was called the "short-story." The hyphen was to stay for some time.

As did Henry James, the kindly sage whose long discourse on central intelligence I was yet to understand. It was an advantage that I was familiar with Chekhov. But weren't his plots rather indeterminate? I sometimes affected the feyness of Chekhov—but this was a weak point, an influence to be rubbed off.

True, "The Road," "The Hollow," "La Cigale," and "The Kiss" had something going for them; you might know what these were. But you had to realize that it was not for nothing that so fashionable a master as W. Somerset Maugham (obviously one of the best paid writers of the day) had dismissed Chekhov as a bad influence. For real instruction, you had to go to Henry James, to Nathaniel Hawthorne, even to Stephen Crane.

Of course, I did have a better time at Stanford than all this would suggest. The truth is that I write here in the abstract.

We made much, for example, of Katherine Mansfield, overlooking even how she had adapted Chekhov's "Sleepyhead" to her ends. Her yearning to adopt a child of Chekhov's did not fail to move me. And I can understand this even today. I believe I can explain, too, Maugham's disapproval of Chekhov—and, for that matter, the idolatry given him by schools of Southeast Asian writers of the early fifties. Saroyan, Steinbeck, and Hemingway equally left their mark—for instance, on the Indonesians. This can be explained too.

In the Stanford of the winter of 1949, Katherine Anne Porter functioned as writer-in-residence, reading, among other preoccupations, James's *A Small Boy and Others*. Such was the lavish banquet that my scholarship year in Palo Alto provided. I couldn't have been more smiled upon by Fortune, considering that during the year before I had had to be satisfied with such crumbs as came my way. I now know, of course, that there was no soul food around to be had.

And to Henry James and company we went eagerly for instruction, guidance, and a sense of "felt" life. So let me recall here my first night at Stanford Village.

It was Sunday, and the shops in nearby Palo Alto were closed. I couldn't possibly get hold of a warm woolen blanket —a predicament which I described to my newly found friends at the dormitory. I slept that night under a borrowed overcoat.

But what did I find on waking, in the light of the winter morning, but three woolen blankets piled one on top of the other over me!

Similarly generous, Stanford kept me out of the intellectual freeze. It helped me write what I consider to this day my first successful story, "A Warm Hand," the twenty-second version of a narrative I had been working on for two straight years and which reflected, in the guise of a voyage, the directions in our society.

Particularly emblanketing in the broad literary daylight was New Criticism. I take note of this here with some affection and gratitude. I couldn't have learned how to see my world without this training. A good story leaves a person not quite as he used to be—of this I had been repeatedly told. You became somehow a different person. Art did just that to you—art, that search for significant form. Or words to that effect. Words, thousands of words.

But how to read was still the problem, and the new discipline taught me this. I could read my own work now in so detached a manner, as though it had been by someone else. It was thus that the twenty-second text of "A Warm Hand" evolved; and to that text the editor of *Sewanee Review* had the kindness to add but two parenthetical commas.

I returned to Manila alert, wearing a new pair of glasses, and disinclined to rejoin the hassle of journalism. It was a "no-no" to work in a weekly, where circulation figures were law. The only possible place of employment was the university. Juan Cabreros Laya, who had won the First Commonwealth Literary Prize for the Novel, with *His Native Soil*, remarked, "I see that you prefer to do the telling now. It didn't seem too long ago that it was you being told something to do!"

He himself had been doing a considerable amount of telling already, in his role as superintendent of schools of Bataan. He was soon to say, "Let's go Tagalog, fellows!"

He had by then already written *This Barangay*, his celebration of the ethic of productive and cooperative life which, alas, appeared to have lost its base in social actuality. Nor in its fictive guise could it appear attractive enough.

IV

THE phrase "Third World" dates back to 1956, by Pierre Jalee's reckoning. It appears to have been applied to countries "that depended neither on the capitalist or socialist system," and hence belonged to "neither of the two worlds." Jalee thinks this is "obviously" wrong.[4] The error, to our mind, is symptomatic of a peculiar kind of innocence in the other two worlds.

We were at the edge of one, to be sure, and shared that innocence too. We were unaware, for example, that we were living out a pattern of literary activity that had been known, though perhaps not appreciated, in Africa. The appreciation was to come from Frantz Fanon, whose writings about the black people were to synthesize the problems we didn't even know existed. Fanon could not possibly have had us in mind, marginal as our efforts were. He had to work with facts from black experience.

Fanon, born in 1925, was hardly in his teens when the annual *The Literary Apprentice* was launched at the University of the Philippines. Could a more revealing name have been found for this journal of the best available writing by a generation that was learning, as had the one that went before it, to excel in the use of the tools of the colonizing culture?

We were using Fanon's calculations, in that initial stage of a triadic pattern that featured efforts to assimilate the occupying culture. In sheer calendar time it would not be long before we reached the second phase, the time when we would experience a "withdrawal and a search for identity." With patience, courage, and imagination, we might then move on to the third stage, which would involve seeking out our own people for instruction and inspiration, and joining our talents with their aspiration and efforts.[5]

Like many other institutions of higher learning in other parts of the country, and indeed like other institutions in other parts of the world, the University of the Philippines (UP) was involved in an industry, serving as the high point in the process the "making of the managerial middle class," to use Ivan D. Illich's phrase. Jean-Paul Sartre would call it "the manufacture of the native elite."[6]

Even to this day, the UP alumni tend to call themselves

"products" of the institution. Some 20,000 of them, according to one estimate, are scattered in the United States; approximately 12,000 more are in various other places in the "First World." Easily 60,000 verified alumni (for the records have not been well kept) bear the stamp "UP Product" and are proud of it.

Their accommodation of the education provided them has been markedly less traumatic than in the case of the blacks, or so would it seem. Of the blacks, Sartre has written:

> They picked out promising adolescents; they branded them, as with a red-hot iron, with the principles of Western culture; they stuffed their mouths full with high-sounding phrases, grand glutinous words that stuck to the teeth.[7]

A lack of training of the kind that leads to the acquisition of the desired brand meant being handicapped in the Creole, *ilustrado,* and *comprador* society that enjoyed the privileged life.

Ramon Magsaysay is said to have acquired the services of a speech tutor in English during his term as president of the Philippines, and this may well be true. He is thought of, not admiringly, as the source of that folksy morsel to the effect that if the high cost of commodities is due to the law of supply and demand, then presidential or legislative powers must be used to "abolish the law"—an implied criticism of his being largely self-educated in the fundamentals of economics.

"One with Shakespeare" was not only the title of Martha Foley's heart-warming story about literary apprenticeship, but for campus literary apprentices themselves, a veritable way of life. We were in search of directions. With the English language as our medium of expression, we felt that Philippine literature was destined to join the mainstream of world letters.

And with the educational programs associated with the name of Senator William Fulbright generating a great deal of meaning for name-droppers, Filipino scholarship could make its mark in the humanities and sciences the world over. But walking the acacia-lined sidewalks of the Florida and Nebraska Streets of Isaac Peral and Padre Faura, how was one to know what was fact and what was illusion?

We were born to a world (at least in the twenties and thirties) for which a specific promise had already been made. And as Bronislav Malinowski puts it,

> This promise has not been redeemed. We are beginning now to see how dangerous it is to speak about the White Man's burden, and to make others shoulder it and carry it for us. We give all the promise implied in our concept of human brotherhood and of equality through education; but when it comes to wealth, power, and self- determination, we refuse this to the other people.[8]

Thus, the Creole, *ilustrado,* and *comprador* can hardly be blamed for holding on to their portions. They could only hold fast to those privileges already won and claim as triumphs of the entire race such tidbits of recognition as the rest of the world allowed them. It is understandable that the Philippines values highly its place in the United Nations,[9] and there is more character portraiture than humor (which must be attributed to the Filipino nation rather than to anyone) in General Romulo's standing before the United Nations General Assembly as its president to deliver an inaugural propped up by a stack of New York City telephone books because he was simply too short for the lectern.[10] Who we were, we didn't quite know. History made this fuzzy for us. We can joke about it now, entrapped as we have been without our being aware of it.

V

MY awareness of what has come into the making of the Filipino begins, if a beginning for this sort of thing is possible at all, in Barcelona. It was the spring of 1965, and Vietnam then was very much in the news.

On this particular morning, the Hotel Manila in Barcelona had the Philippine flag on display. It was its red field instead of the blue, however, that was in the top position—meaning "war," as every Filipino high school student knows. Frantic inquiries, which flustered not a few of the Hotel Manila clerks, indicated that there had been a mistake. Nothing resembling a global war had occurred. It was simply the hotel's way of signifying that this was Sunday. The manager promised that the error would be corrected, and we walked away feeling quite self-righteous.

A surprise awaited us at the corner bookstore, where we had gone shortly to browse. We saw there a copy of *Heroes Filipinos*, a magnificent piece of bookmanship listing the Spanish soldiers and civilians who, at some time or other during Spain's long stay in the Philippines, had died in the country. The biographies made up a compendium of two columns to the page, two inches thick; and they suggested a meaning for the term "Filipino" quite different from the one I had always known.

Later I was told of the connotation of "picaresque," "pushy," even "brusque," that the word "Filipino" seemed to have for the Madrileño. And Quijano de Manila was to describe, in an excellent series of essays that were later to appear in book form,[11] how at some point in our history the word took on a larger import.

He set the date as somewhere before either 1872 or 1896, when the word "Filipino" had the same sense as "Creole." As an offshoot of the "civil war" between the two kinds of Spaniards that were then comfortably settled in the Philippines, the word got further burnished.

The occasion was a small object lesson in self-interest. On one hand were the early comers who had made the country their newfound land; on the other were the late arrivals, beneficiaries of the opening of the Suez Canal. Although these two groups were the ruling class vis-a-vis the "Indios," clashes between them were inevitable.[12]

Had Rizal written his novels, *Noli Me Tangere* and *El Filibusterismo*, during a period of greater freedom, his portraits of that ruling class might have contained less caricature, less propaganda. But the novels reflect Quijano de Manila's view, however objectively Rizal may have wished to disguise the theme of self-interest.

This is not perhaps the place for even the briefest resume of the circumstances around the Cavite Mutiny and the involvement of Fathers Jose Burgos, Mariano Gomez, and Jacinto Zamora. But February 17, 1872 should be remembered, for their martyrdom on that day "transformed" the meaning of the word "Filipino." That day "witnessed the full emergence of the idea of the Filipino...when the people —country folk and city folk, peon and *ilustrado*, Creole and Indio—spontaneously assembled en masse to turn what should have been a warning into an event so ominous that the Spaniards fled in terror behind the walls of Intramuros. It was already a nation that hailed the three priests as 'our parents' and the people that chose those words must have known what they proclaimed."[13]

The schoolboy's image of *barangays* monsoon-borne from the south does not fit easily with the impression conveyed by that February morning in 1872. Today, as then, Manila is not the Philippines. In lifestyle, if nothing else, the difference between the Manilan and the *provinciano* is one not to be minimized or overlooked. When it appears in literature, it is an error to dismiss it as merely typical of city and country antinomy!

There is among provincial people no genuine folk memory of their seafaring ancestors. One suspects that the line, "I am a Filipino, pride of the Malay race," which schoolboys have been urged to memorize, is· typical city-school rhetoric; indeed, it has been pressed into service in elocution classes. And when searching for "Filipino culture," the investigator does not probe into the Manila lifestyle but into that of the provinces. When yet richer styles than imaginable are sought, one goes to a different country

altogether—to that of the Ifugao, the Bagobo, or the Maguin-
danao.

It is no small irony that it has been folk such as these,
who may be described as the most un-Filipino, that have
supplied those elements in the national culture which have
been much valued as distinctly Filipino. We might say, then,
that the Creole-*ilustrado-comprador* combination makes us
one group. At the opposite end we find the non-Christian.
But this is not quite all of it, for there is a middle group. Its
members are not readily distinguishable by their physical
features or costume. They are quite difficult to describe
except in terms of their efforts at social mobility—at becoming at least *ilustrado.*

Schooling, for such as these, is the bridge by which the
crossing is made. They have found it to be a terribly narrow
one. The approach, if mythically on high ground, is in the
squatter areas of Manila and other cities.[14] And there the hour
of the day is always twilight, contrary to what the National
Anthem claims:

Land of the morning,
Child of the sun returning...

But it must be admitted that with relentless fervor,
millions make the try; yet more millions remain ill-provisioned
or too dispirited to make the move.

Theirs is the continuing dusk of subsistence living at
barrio, swidden, or *aplaya* level.

VI

John Galbraith has said of India that it is "the beginning
of wisdom...to realize that it is not a country but a continent."[15] Paraphrasing this, we might say that understanding
the Philippines begins in the realization that it is one nation

made up of three countries.

Manila is the capital of the first country, which is the City. The second country—the Barrio—has a capital known by many names: Aplaya, Bondok, Wawa—whatever. And these names do not celebrate a dubious piety—like San Felipe, San Roque, etc.—but somehow honor this very life of the land, calling Nature, as it were, by its true name.

The third country—the Mountain—by its very nature needs no capital or center, although it shares with the Barrio a calculated distance from the city.

It is at this point where we must let Galbraith's kind knowledge of India contribute a further insight:

> Most Indians live in the villages and directly draw their living from the land. They pay taxes. Some of their sons go off to the cities or to the Army. Almost all listen to a transistor radio...Yet the Indian village is not much governed either by New Delhi or the Capital of its state. Nor is it governed in any actual sense by itself. It lives by an accepted code of behavior, not by formal law. This is better. The people of India learned centuries ago to hope for the least possible attention from higher levels of government.... The self-sufficiency of the village was its strength; to be left alone was its greatest good fortune. The lesson of centuries is not soon unlearned.[16]

Read the above passage to a Filipino, taking care, however, to change "Indian" to "Filipino." Instead of the sentence about transistor radios, you might say: "Almost all like to drink Coca-Cola, listen to American music, and see Hollywood movies..." and, of course, you would substitute "Manila" for "New Delhi." Thus you complete the disguise.

The observation so fits the Philippines as well. "How can that be?" you ask. Then you realize that both the barrio and Galbraith's Indian village belong to a particular part of Asia, the Asia of underdeveloped societies. We share a transgeographical and transcultural community of peoples asking of History and of the future fairly similar questions.

To become aware of our history is to become aware
of our singularity. It is a moment of reflective repose
before we devote ourselves to action again.[17]

Thus Octavio Paz, reflecting on the life and thought of his
native Mexico, and clearing part of the ground for us as well.
For besides sharing a past in which Spain is at the center of
experience, Mexico and the Philippines have not infrequently
provided each other with appreciable features for comparison.

In this instance, however, comparison will not work. For
in the course of his musing, Octavio Paz came to this conclusion:

...I considered my questions, like those of others, to
be a cowardly excuse for not facing reality; I also felt
that all our speculations about the supposed character
of the Mexican were nothing but subterfuges of our
impotence as creators.

At several points in our own effort to understand the
problems of creativity in the Philippine context, I came to
more or less the same conclusion. But now I doubt its
validity. Although Octavio Paz, speaking of the situation in
Mexico, found

...that an inferiority complex influenced our Mexican
preference for analysis, and that the meagerness of
our creative output was due not so much to the
growth of critical faculties at the expense of our
creativity as it was to our instinctive doubts about our
abilities.[18]

This is not true with regard to the Philippines. Indeed, the
singularity of the Philippines needs some attention. Mexican
reality cannot be altered by contemplation, according to
Octavio Paz. What is needed is to plunge "ourselves into
them."

I submit, however, that thought is action. And thinking is

plunging into just that which Conrad's moral concern identifies as "the destructive element."

In this situation, perhaps one is forced to raise somewhat difficult questions. "Is there any sense to our history?" "Where did it all go wrong?" "Why are we, of all people, doomed to exchange one despotism for another in seemingly unbroken succession?"[19]

These are Michael Glenny's, the promptings on how Alexander Solzhenitsyn might have seized upon, and committed himself to, the subject of his *August 1914.* I find that one has only to adopt a meaning of despotism in terms of one's own experience for the rhetoric to dissipate and for the practical applicability as probing tools of these questions to become apparent.

For, in the Philippine experience, History has provided its own despotism. Where did things go wrong? To which you might reply that one such point, quite possibly, was when English was adopted as a national language.

We cannot go into the story of the national language problem here. Suffice it to recall that by the mid-twenties Spanish had begun to make room for English in the country. We of the Barrio—for it is to that country that I belong— acquired thereby a double inferiority as, with a symbolic *maleta* in hand, we trudged in the direction of the country of the City.

Our first difficulty involved the medium of expression already beginning to become more and more preferred in government and business. This was English, which had already become the medium of instruction in the public school system. The second difficulty concerned the economic and political privileges which our betters enjoyed by accident of having been born in the City.

For in most underdeveloped nations, a principal center of population, often the capital city, sets the level of the aspirations of the nation as a whole. The psychology of underdeveloped peoples has much to do with this.[20]

But neither to us nor, I believe, to the citizens of the City, was yet another inferiority revealed—one which had been built into the social structure, related to the nation's colonial past and neocolonial future.

Silenced with jail terms and various sorts of politically motivated harassments for expressing the then current anti-American sentiments in the Tagalog theater and in poetry, writers began to see a less than promising future in the pursuit of Tagalog letters except as journalists. Years later, the nostalgia attributed to those days, the early and mid-twenties, reflected a deep sense of loss. The old-guard Tagalog writers speak even today of a Golden Age.

"A man who has a language possesses the world expressed and implied by that language," wrote Frantz Fanon, in *Black Skin, White Masks*.[21] For a barrio youth of the early twenties, then, to have control of Spanish, the language used by the class already enjoying the circumstances of a life superior to those of people in his immediate environment—to master that language, to speak it, to be heard, even, in the country of the City—what could be a natural and reasonable aspiration?

Beyond the scope of his mind, of course, was the fact that the country of the City had by then been colonized anew. This had to be recognized, and to be responded to as well.

> Every colonized people—in other words, every people in whose soul an inferiority complex has been created by the death and burial of its cultural originality—finds itself face to face with the language of the civilizing nation; that is, with the culture of the mother country.[22]

This, says Fanon, is what one must live with as a people for whom history has provided a colonizing culture.

The process is intriguing. Research, Fanon hopes, might some day reveal the changes in the flesh, even in the composition of the body fluids, of those concerned. The colonized, he asserts, becomes whiter as he renounces his blackness, his jungle. In the French colonial army, and particularly in the Senegalese regiments, the black officers serve first of all as interpreters. They are used to convey the master's orders to their fellows, and they enjoy a certain position of honor.[23]

In our country of the City that position of honor, of privilege, even of power, was all too clearly manifest through the use of English. English had become the new vehicle of expression and was soon to conscript promoters of the new master's voice.

By the time I was fifteen, I "heard" nothing else. To be sure, my beginnings were in the small harbor town of Romblon and the backwoods of Mindoro. But my response to the "orders" must have become second nature. When my grandfather gave me a gift of three pesos one day, I promptly transformed the money into a Funk and Wagnall's desk dictionary. I must admit that today this is not too much of a feat. But if it is understood that Romblon is a copra-buying town, that it did not boast a bookstore, then that dictionary is no meaningless cultural item. I sent for the book from none other than the all-too-happily-named book distribution firm in Manila, the Philippine Education Company.

Within and in the vicinity of the City itself the orders were better heard, better responded to. The citizens of that country were being made secure by the Filipinization policy that had been adopted by the American administration. But under the cover of political autonomy, something else was happening.

VII

THE Filipino has this continuing task: to make available a representation of the triadic national community provided by History. What the representation is he could not have known in the thirties, except through sheer inexplicable talent; only the fifties were to provide the aesthetics he needed, if he wanted to be instructed, or to discover them on his own.

The making of his national community was, in any case, something he could not have been aware. The Depression years were no occasion for any kind of searching. The nation's *comprador* and managerial classes were then deep into more autonomy, more Philippine-ness. The English language provided the rhetoric for the movement, and with just as much help as it had earlier been provided the ambiguities that made the movement necessary.

Independence as soon as a stable government had been achieved? A calculated ambiguity, no less. And it provided us schoolboys of the Barrio with the patriotism to contribute twenty centavos each to the annual drive for funds. From quite a different motivation, we allowed ourselves to be fined five or ten centavos on every occasion that the school "spies" caught us shifting to the vernacular—or, in Fanon's terms, every time we asserted ourselves.

It is a sad story, and the business of fines for speaking the vernacular remained until the sixties. The Filipino writer must write about this as well as other facets of the national reality; and the task is not easy. It never is in any language, let alone a borrowed one.

The stories in *Seven Hills Away* and the novel *A Season of Grace* speak of the country of the Barrio that I have been trying to delineate. My Creole, *ilustrado*, and *comprador* readers must have seen their validity; and for this I am bound by gratitude to a statue: that of Jose Rizal, which stood in the center of the Romblon town plaza, its back (characteristically) to our eighteenth-century Catholic church.

Thus it stood, this representation of the national genius, concrete gray in the sun-mottled shade of the acacias. The figure had deep mythic import for me: a Rizal in a heavy overcoat, and in a pensive pose, the left foot brought slightly forward, two thick books to one side.

I do not remember the kind of shoes; and whether the

sculptor had provided a hat escapes me. The figure did have a vest, fully buttoned. Anyway, all this epitomized for me the power of the written word, the durability of books, and the need for travel and, in due course, an overcoat.

I was to stand in Rizal's debt even more directly when, as a beginning magazine writer in Manila, I had to fall back on the Rizal material collected at the National Library. There I discovered the letters, the postcards, the marginalia of a martyred life.

All grist for my mill. The pieces I wrote from them kept me in bed and board for weeks on end—while the Mindoro stories were being composed in a tenement I shared with my parents. We lived then in a street, in the Sta. Cruz district, called Kusang-Loob, which translates, literally, as "initiative."

As Fanon might have put it, Rizal won himself a psychic bride in Josephine Bracken. As a struggling freelance writer, I discovered those psychic girlfriends of Rizal's that preceded Josephine.

My first efforts at fiction, meanwhile, were quickly turned down by the *ilustrado* editors; but two were accepted and published in *Philippine Magazine*, which even at the time had already become an institution.[24] Its editor was A.V.H. Hartendorp, and acceptance of one's work by him, however heavily the manuscript was edited (which was most certainly the fate that met every single one of my efforts), was nevertheless a psychic success.

With a by-line in *Philippine Magazine*, one could say that one had arrived. The import of this, however, was beyond our grasp at that time; and by "our" I mean my contemporaries as well.

Let me digress. The discipline which of late has been tagged "English as a Second Language" reminds me of another observation of Fanon's:

> In the white world the man of color encounters difficulties in the development of his body schema.[25]

English is, after all, *the* white world. Communication or

speech, after all, is an item in the bodily schema. And so to proceed with Fanon:

> The body is surrounded by an atmosphere of certain uncertainty. I know that if I want to smoke, I shall have to reach out my right arm and take the pack of cigarettes lying at the table. The matches, however, are on the left and I shall have to lean back slightly. And all these movements are made not out of habit but out of implicit knowledge. A slow composition of myself as a body in the middle of a spatial and temporal world—such seems to be the schema. It does not impose itself on me; it is, rather, a definitive structuring of the self and of the world—definitive because it creates a dialectic between my body and the world.[26]

Did I say "English as a Second Language?" For my generation, and for the others before and after my time, the problem that Fanon suggests embodies a condition of our lives. Remember the five- or twenty-centavo fines for every non-English word spoken on the school premises? What a severely tightening bolt in the structure that must have been, and we did not know it!

In any event, it was the English language, so readily adopted by the country of the City—the better for its citizenry to remain comfortable and secure in the places where they already stood, and the better for the American regime to put the country together in whatever way profitable—this was the process, the "slow composition" of ourselves toward a national expression.

In those continuous adjustments necessary for the arm to reach for that mythic cigarette or match, don't we now see one explanation for the rather minimal scholarship or imaginative creativity that our generation can lay claim to? And to think that from one-fourth to a third of the national income is generally invested in public instruction—in a borrowed language...

A double difficulty, admitting the inefficiency of the

system and its conduct in a borrowed medium. Ivan D. Illich demonstrates the first level of this phenomenon in terms of Latin America.[27] The Philippines should come forward and volunteer its public school system as an example of the further turn of the screw.

For the Filipino taxpayer contributes liberally to matters of the mind that keep him and his fellows in their proper places—which is, in the nature of things, on a rung of the ladder lower than some other. Even as this is written, the liberating effect of a native language providing the rhetoric of a national culture has only begun to dawn on the elected spokesmen of the nation. An earlier Constitutional Convention in Manila, it will be recalled, had resolved the national language problem in favor of keeping the status quo, with Arabic in that category as well. "If we adopted Tagalog," remarked a delegate who had been asked by the San Francisco consulate to update the resident exiles about our then constitution-in-the-making, "we would generate a sort of internal imperialism."

Two choices were actually involved, we countered,—two imperialisms—one imported and continuing, the other home-grown. There was no doubt, however, that the elite, as represented by the duly elected members of the constitutional convention, had learned their lesson—true products of the system that they are.

VIII

QUITE possibly, I have been fortunate. Besides having enjoyed a spotty tuition in what could well be the more crucial of my formative years, I did reading on my own, locating the voices I could listen to for some reason or other and walking away from the rest because of something threatening or, perhaps, unfamiliar. I still cannot enjoy Gide, for example, outside of a couple of his short novels, *Strait is the Gate* and *Pastoral Symphony,* perhaps.

Victorian novels were always a pain. My interests were in Knut Hamsun, Emil Salinpaa, and Jean Giono, and Liam O'Flaherty and Maurice O'Sullivan. While not underestimating the deficiencies of this exposure, I have to exploit its advantage. My authors were (and are) not in the standard menu of the college library cafeteria—wherever that may be, in Manila or elsewhere.

Their unintended anti-academism must have appealed to me, although here I must confess to having been shocked at learning that the author of *Twenty Years Agrowing,* a first and only book, had to join later on a Civic Guards company in Dublin. But my authors were, in any case, writing about things I knew; their books served me well in providing the self-confidence I needed. Their pages concerned a reality as distant from me as that about which I tried to write, my borrowed language having separated each actuality from me at every moment of composition. My merest jottings were notes not so much from an underground as from another world.

Out of those emerged the episodes that comprised *The Winds of April.* and the *Seven Hills Away.* The life I described quite literally spoke a different language—and became a different life. Rendered in an alien tongue, that life attained the distinction of a translation even before it had been made into a representation of· reality, and then even before becoming a reality of its own.

The English language thus had the effect of continually presenting that life as non-actual, even as it affirmed the insecurity of its making. I tried to evoke life, and no sooner was that done than I denied its very being through my rendering of it in a foreign tongue—believing that that was the way to the truth. And in affirming, how I uttered denials as well!

Yet the impulse to create a world through language also told me that in borrowing I might be giving, that my taking obliged a giving of another gift in turn.

But you could not have put it that way then, let alone think up so circuitous a justification. You merely wanted to do that story or that poem for Mr. Hartendorp, for *Philippine Magazine*, or to get the story to A.E. Litiatco for *Graphic*. You did not have the advantage, enjoyed by other contributors, of having been taught by T. Inglis Moore (M.A. Cantab., right?), whose lectures were infused with a rapture and informed enchantment not easily dispelled by the sound of *calesa* and *caretella*[28] traffic on Padre Faura.

The *Graphic* catered to the high-school and post-high-school reading public scattered throughout the country, an audience hardly made for a big circulation figure. Some 25,000 copies a week represented a high point; if the figure dropped by 500, the fault was the literary editor's. He had allowed an obscure filler of a poem to be published. I was to sweat out the same hassle some ten years later, editing a similar weekly for the same publishing firm.

As for the *Philippine Magazine*, its interests were anthropological and broadly political; folklore was its stock-in-trade. It was easily the only place in the country where T. Inglis Moore could publish his novel about the Ifugaos. This ran serially, giving the editor many a breathless weekend on account of delayed installments. The circulation was something like 7,000 or 8,000 but it was a magazine widely read and respected by the country's decision-makers.

Mr. Hartendorp was, of course, decidedly for English, which he called "the greatest gift America has made to the Philippines; given English, everything else that America had brought would in time have come anyway." His description of the efforts that the Filipino imagination expended cannot be read today too objectively:

> For some years the writers wasted their time writing imitations of such tales of adventure and plot and stories embodying sophisticated dialog as they saw in American and foreign magazines. Others tried to write tales of the remote past, involving shadowy legendary figures, and drawing largely upon their imaginations

for development. These efforts failed as they deserved to fail. Then they began to write of their own people and of their own times, tales of the country folk and of the provincial village, tales of the jungle and sea and river, tales of Manila; and they found their metier. They began naturally to write a sort of story strangely like the Russian stories that have become classics, probably because the great Russian writers were among the first to see the human interest, the comedy and the tragedy, the truth and the beauty in the everyday life of the people, and probably also because the Russians have in them something of the Oriental.[29]

As I quote these lines, I have on my desk a copy of *Children of the Soil*, an anthology of Philippine short stories in Russian translation. The book was produced in 1970 by Nauka Publishers in association with the Institute of Oriental Studies of the Academy of Sciences of the USSR; its colophon includes the information that Nauka issued 30,000 copies. Twenty writers are represented in the anthology, including twelve others whose works have been limited to Tagalog and have therefore never been read outside the Philippines. These Tagalog stories have never even been translated into English in Manila. There may well be some form of cultural elitism here, or perhaps it is merely the operation of the law of supply and demand. Mr. Hartendorp, in any case, saw a relevance and took the trouble to make a note of it—namely, that there was a similarity between our "sort of story" and that of the Russians. All told, the two or three collections of Philippine writings that have been issued in the United States do not add up, in number of copies printed, to this single title of Nauka's.

Already, Hartendorp's 1937 essay goes on to say, our stories have been published or are being republished in the world press. Moreover,

Foreign writers visiting Manila are without exception surprised—and impressed. To many of them it seems impossible that Filipinos should be writing in English as if they think in English, such is the case; and why shouldn't it be after over thirty years of English in the public schools?[30]

The best part of it all was that Hartendorp was proud of his work, proud of his writers, and proud of his adopted country. A visit to his office on the top floor of the Uy Tet Building in Binondo was a high point in one's progress from the Barrio to the City. A young writer might have tea with the old man, and such conversation as transpired might find space some weeks later in the editor's famous "Four O'Clock in the Editor's Office" column.

Two excerpts from the January 1937 "Four O'Clock" may suggest to the reader the quality of life in those days:

> For Christmas, I received a box of cigars from one young lady, one of the *Magazine* authors, whom I never met personally, and when I asked her in a note of thanks how she knew I smoked she replied that "all editors smoke"...also a letter conveying the season's greetings from Jose Garcia Villa in which he said: "I am glad to see a magazine like the *National Review* in the Islands; that increases the number of our intelligent magazines to two. Imagine that. Our first snow fell today. Which reminds me I should like indeed to visit Manila. Mr. Quezon should send me a round-trip ticket for the good of the nation. Let him realize that and his soul is saved..." The letter was dated November 24, from New York City.

* * * *

In his ranking of Philippine short stories for 1936, Villa gives the *Philippine Magazine* a total of 30 points as against 43 for the *Tribune* (daily and weekly) and 44 for the *Graphic* (weekly) and he lists only one story from the *Philippine Magazine*...in his "Roll of Honor." He again "stars" heavily what he called the "experimental" stories. I don't quarrel with him over that...[31]

And nobody could have told you then that all this was provincial. There were other knighthoods to win, other nobilities to meet: Martha Foley, Whit Burnett, Edward J. O'Brien—names you saw in books. Strongholds like *Story Magazine* and *Scribners'*—and at whose gates Manuel E. Arguilla and Jose Garcia Villa duly arrived and crashed. Villa having already left the country and settled in the United States, *Philippine Magazine's* import for us diminished with every recognition that he won in Manhattan.

IX

IT is in this context of aspirations—whether achieved or not—that our generation's short-lived interest in writing in Tagalog must be seen. The impetus for change was provided by the war. The rigors of the Japanese Occupation did not quite break the illusion. The war, in fact, provided a new level of hope.

"We would write of it—and now!" we told ourselves. And such writing was later attained by Stevan Javellana (*Without Seeing the Dawn*),[32] Celso Carunungan (*Like a Big Brave Man*),[33] and Edilberto K. Tiempo (*Watch in the Night*).[34] The novel about the conflict of Spanish and American cultures that Edward J. O'Brien had expected of Villa was not to appear now (or ever?), for Villa[35] had begun to devote his time to poetry. Earlier, Carlos Bulosan, who belonged to the Barrio if ever anyone did, had published *The Laughter of My Father*,[36] which American readers thought amusing and literally promising—a reaction which must be judged with the Japanese Occupation of the Philippines in the back of one's mind.

In any case, the stage seemed to have been set; the audience was soon to gasp over the charms of the idiosyncratic, eccentric, and even avant-grade. This happy response was to be ushered in with Dame Edith Sitwell's recognition of Villa's work. The City's abundant dreams had begun to find an embodiment.

The process, it must be noted, had not been all that easy. It had been a case of "slow composition." The boys had gone through all the phases. The match had been there; the cigarette case had to be reached for. The cigarette itself was not the local kind—say, *Pagkakaisa*, its paper seemingly laced with molasses. It turned out to be the kind that was filtered, mentholated—sanitary! Quite a distance from the actuality of the country that produced some of the world's best cigars.

But, for all this, it was a far cry from the what-might-have-been. I recall a conversation with V.S. Pritchett in his flat in London, in the fall of 1965. Quite casually—and accidentally—Pritchett allowed himself to remark: "It is good to have to be colonized. For your country now does have some roads!"

It is just possible that I quote him erroneously—my memory is not too trustworthy. But perhaps it is the unsaid in which we should be interested.

Pritchett's sentiments in matters that concern us here are of a different nature, as will be noted later. In any case, the publishing record must be seen in some such light as this. As Fanon has pointed out, the first chapter of black history—as it is understood in the white world—deals with cannibalism.

With what does the first chapter of Filipino history begin in the mind of the white reader?

To millions of school children, with Lapu-Lapu and Magellan. The white adult, and with what? The G-string, paganism, the original tree-house. The common feature here is the G-string, or substitutes thereof.

And so when Villa made it with the sanctifying benediction of Dame Edith, the event could not be anything but sheer History. As in the case of black writing, from which Fanon drew his observations, the first stage of the triadic development began.

X

THE "slow composition"—"a definitive structuring of the self"—these words bear their quiet authority.

For the Chicano boy named Carlos in an Arizona grade school, it means learning to be called Chuck and saying in English what is needed to make it known that he must go to the washroom; to fail in that is to wet his pants and keep his secret all through the school day...

Many have had equivalent experience at more complicated levels of self-expression. Ivor Winter's criticism of Amador T. Daguio's free verse—that the samples to hand had their equivalent in what one might contrive from the vocabulary of the San Francisco telephone directory—caused this Filipino poet, then already in his forties, to fall into a fit of depression for days.

How deep are the roots of this despair? The definitive structure appears to be a question of bone and muscle, of breath and sinew. While a change of language can be done by fiat, a command remains, unfortunately, a command. It is not without significance that the phrase "mother tongue"— with connotations of "mother country" and in use since 1645, according to the OED—can not quite match in richness its Tagalog equivalent, *wikang sinuso*, literally, the language that is breast-fed.

It seems that with English, a near-total restructuring is needed. Our educational system used to advantage the vernaculars, thanks to the now famous Iloilo Experiment, and this demonstrated how much more quickly the school child can build from a native vocabulary base. The logistical problems of obtaining books in the vernacular, as well as the rethinking required to make English textbooks useful (instead of resorting to the customary, all-too-easy translation), have increased the drop-out rate. Thus, the boost in illiteracy has been erroneously attributed to the use of the vernacular; and, ironically, the use of English has found greater support for the wrong reasons.

As a professional group, our writers have not been too concerned with this problem. More relevant to their efforts is the work at hand, which must make·its uncertain way into the world. Villa had shown the way—or, part of the way, in any case. But the enterprise has been attended by such uncertainty that the search for standards became yet another source of frustration.

English departments in universities and colleges all over the country were of one mind about providing the aspirants with images of success. We were "being offered tips as to how to get your teeth into the creamy part of the cake," as David Caute has put it (albeit in another context). "We live, horribly, in the manipulative society. In the nineteenth-century authoritarian regimes you were lashed on the back if you forgot your place; in the twentieth-century totalitarian regimes you are convinced day and night that your place (or two places up the queue) is the one you have chosen for yourself."[37]

We chose English, didn't we? Villa's announcement cannot be faulted as inappropriate: "Have Come, Am Here," his book said right on the cover.[38]

But every reading is a heaven-sent opportunity for misreading. The record is incontrovertible. Recently, in the *London Times Literary Supplement*, I found this note concerning two translated Russian novels:

> *Astride a Dolphin* is tolerably well translated but the English of *White Grass* is full of ineptitudes. The use of 'pal', for instance, might pass if the whole book were to be thought of as in American English, but it isn't... Progress Publishers ought to make up their minds whether they want translations into American English or English English, and it would probably help if they always had the work checked by natives who are either still resident in their country or have

only very recently left it.[39]

The residence requirement is a new turn in the style game. How unfortunate of Progress Publishers that they have not been in a position to learn from our experience in the Philippines.

For it was not until the mid-sixties that we could stage a literary contest without a native-born American performing as a valued member of the jury. And more sincere and obliging gentlemen than those we tapped for these chores you could not have found. Indeed, they obliged, as kindred souls would; they inspected many a pound of unlaundered prose (much like what you are now reading) and not only chose for us the year's blue-ribboned typewriter but affirmed the healthy growth as well of a Philippine Literature in English.

Dutifully, our editors printed, in italics and boxed in with decorative borders, intermittent reports of prose and verse that had seen the light of print abroad.[40] Both Delfin Freznosa and I contributed to *Life and Letters* (London); but what happened? The magazine became defunct. One cannot make much of a cause-and-effect relationship there, but the tidbit might just be instructive.

In truth, young man, we have found them out! But behave as if you're innocent. As a youth, I was so backward as to think that proofreaders did their job by plucking out the lead that made up a line of type and checking on the letters upside down. I have learned about proofs and galley sheets since, having spent nights at printing plants whose owners never heard of overtime pay for mechanics and magazine writers alike.

Be on guard. Don't make the mistakes we did. Don't fall into the trap we got into! The smell of print? A lot of bull that is! History did have that trap ready for us. But look, we've unsprung it, we've snapped the thing off! There! You can move on now. The thing can't work anymore.

Consider the scene: Fanon, after doing a lecture on Negro and European poetry in French, is approached by an acquaintance. "At bottom," says this Frenchman, "you are a white man." But Fanon is not misled into accepting this "honorary citizenship."[41]

This is done all the time. Andre Breton once said of Aime Cesaire: "Here is a black man who handles the French language as no white man today can."[42]

Equivalent accolades have been delivered on various occasions, for various reasons, and almost always they have reflected the truth except for one nagging qualification: they incorporate an odd mixture of hope and doubt expressed with an equally odd mixture of sincere admiration and patronage. Thus, to Alfred Kazin, V.S. Naipaul is the deserved heir of Joseph Conrad's stylistic gifts.[43]

John Updike raises some expectations:

> Has not black music, via jazz and rock, transformed the ears of the world? Did not African masks inspire Cubism and destroy forever the sweet face that had reigned in European art from Giotto to Renoir? More to the point, have not rural societies, such as Russia, Ireland, and the American South, historically poured fresh vernacular energy and heroic simplicity into Europe's tired mainstream of literature?...So might we not expect, as the post-colonial generations take their place among the world bourgeoisie, a passionate intelligentsia to arise and enunciate native truths, to embody a living reality that has hitherto been seen only through white eyes?[44]

Updike goes on, rightfully, to acclaim Chinua Achebe's "beautiful economy" in his portrait (in *Things Fall Apart*) of the breakup, under colonialism, of tribal society, showing that "space had been cleared, an understanding had been achieved, a new beginning was implied." But Updike cannot help asking a rather pointed question, to which he also gives a dour reply:

> For whom are the works written, in the languages of departed occupiers? Not for the "nigger trash" still

sunk in the tribal dream and the struggle for sustenance. Or for the African whites, ever more anachronistically clinging to their plantations and prerogatives and the nineteenth-century credos that justified them. At the moment, the black African artist, from his niche in American colleges or Paris literary circles, seems a voice without an auditorium, a sensibility between worlds.[45]

Something more complex than the finding of a "voice without an auditorium" appears to have happened, not only in Africa but in Asia as well.

In the Philippines, we lost our sense of direction; and when we appeared to have found it, we were unprepared to recognize not only the presence of language barriers but, even more so, the presence of those of class or varieties of class. And all this had its necessary effect on the art we wanted to practice.

Every item on the recognition scoreboard deflected the true north by so many degrees. I have already alluded to Edward J. O'Brien's expectations of Villa. One wonders what he would have said at the appropriate time of the careers of Gabriel Garcia Marquez or Jorge Luis Borges.

For just about then Carlos Bulosan began to find an American audience. His stories were tagged accordingly as efforts that "represented a search for the realities of his past" —and as authentically "ethnic," "interesting," and "quaint." They elicited the requisite "My, what a remarkable talent to have come from such a background."[46] Other writers surfaced from the blue of the Pacific: Celso Carunungan's *Like a Big Brave Man* followed Javellana's *Without Seeing the Dawn,* and then came Wilfredo Nolledo's *But for the Lovers.*[47] Shades of a renaissance here! To dress Updike's thoughts in different imagery, might not the footwork of the *tinikling* one day replace the latest dance step?

But there should be no fear of that. Our efforts, alas, appear fated to be marginal. We seem to be shortwinded, unable to pursue any continuing passion. Fr. Miguel Bernad finds our literature "perpetually inchoate."[48] Perhaps we have only set a "brush fire"—in California, an unhappy event, and in our own words a *ningas kugon*, which is a conflagration of annoyingly frustrating brevity. Or, could this be an aspect of that process of "slow composition"—of the continuing non-definitive restructuring that Fanon has observed?

XI

IF every reading is an opportunity for misreading, it takes on also the features of crucial class encounter. Two might write for the same audience—say, that of the *New Yorker*—only to discover that each inhabits a different world.

From James Thurber's own testimony, for example, comes a glimpse of a difference between his and Harold Ross's station. In an "opinion sheet" that Ross attached to a Thurber manuscript, the following was set down:

1. You start a story like this off without a suburban plant and a reader assumes you're talking about metropolitan apartment house life, and is fairly surprised when he comes to a passage about someone going upstairs.[49]

To be sure, certain Tagalog editors have asked their writers to provide details with similar care. For instance, the writer must furnish a stone fence or an iron gate, and even perhaps a watchdog, in every instance in which he has to describe—and make convincing—a rich man's house.

Editors, in short, do share some occupational diseases. But to continue with the Thurber case:

2. You might, if you want, clinch the suburban atmosphere by putting in here the name of some town in the region—Rye, or some Connecticut town.

3. You never later have the people sitting down to dinner, nor do you take any notice whatever of

dinner. If you make cocktails and buffet dinner, there is no question in the reader's mind at all, and it seems to me the kind of function the Spencers would give—as I did in my younger days...

For indeed, we read into the text at hand whatever our own experience seems to help create the illusion more fully. Thurber thought little of his story, however. He even got around to liking "it so little" that he "never included it in a book"—and he might have been right at that, since whether it was buffet or dinner would have been Ross's choice.

V.S. Pritchett tells of an even more interesting editorial experience in connection with one story of his, "A Sense of Humor." It had been turned down "by all likely publications in England and America." Pritchett had to put it away, "feeling that (he) had made one more bloomer."

He goes on to write: "Then, after a year or so, Lehman's *New Writing* appeared and he published it. I got £3 for the story. I cannot say that I woke up to find myself famous but I had modestly arrived."[50]

What was behind the long wait before publication and recognition? From his special knowledge as a writer and critic, Pritchett reveals the answer:

> Up till now in English literature the "uncommon" people had been presented as "characters," usually comic. I had a curious conversation with H.G. Wells about this. I asked him to tell me about Gissing, who had taken his working-class and lower-middle class people seriously, so that to my mind he was closer to the Russian tradition than ours. Wells began in his sporty way: "The trouble with Gissing was that he thought there was a difference between a woman and a lady, but we all know there is no difference at all."[51]

Pritchett then asked whether it might be possible "to present, say, a lower-middle-class man or woman seriously and not as a comic character." Mr. Wells reflected and then said "No."

Pritchett's Edwardian London, then, had quite simply gotten in the way of their understanding each other. Characters of fiction believed by an artist of one class to be genuinely normal human beings may well be eccentrics to his fellow artist who belong to another class. Recalling his own background, Pritchett writes:

> I was brought up differently, I had been to school with working-class boys and girls. My parents and relations, my grandfather the bricklayer, my eccentric great uncle the cabinet-maker, my mother the shop girl, and my father the errand boy and shop assistant in Kentish Town, had belonged originally to this (the working) class.

His late start was a sheer case of misreading, Pritchett suggests. His interest had been in depicting

> revelations of a nature and (rather in Ibsen's fashion) exposing the illusions or received ideas by which people live or protect their dignity. On the other hand, in the preoccupation with common speech which I suppose I owe to my storytelling mother and to listening closely to Spaniards and others abroad, I did not allow more than I could help the documentary realism that was fashionable in the Thirties. The storyteller either digests or contemplates life for his own purposes. It is a flash that suddenly illuminates and then passes.[52]

Rare, however, is the reader who can see and respond to that illumination. Even as we teach in college courses the short story, we are deep in the culture of a counter-sensibility in which many things just are not as readily possible as we thought they might be. The TV serials, the movies, the day-to-day surprises and boredoms that are standard fare to the sensibilities, becloud that illumination, that sense of import that the artist builds into his art.

I have called this difficulty the Gooseberry Problem, after

Chekhov's story "The Gooseberries," where, as readers may remember, we have a story within a story—a story within a frame. Most critics and professional commentators forget the uniqueness of this structure, limiting their attention to what is within the frame and forgetting that the frame is part of the story. Rather than take cognizance of the entire structure, the hasty reader allows for the inner part only. Overlooking the larger, outer structure leads to the critical error of "distancing."

While it has made for comforting insights, "distancing" merely provides the reader with his own agreeable fiction. At present, this idea is probably anything but acceptable in the critical establishment. But it is a point that the Third World intelligence cannot yield, for to do so is to accept willingly being overlooked altogether.

When Edward J. O'Brien granted the validity of the storyteller's voice,[53] he must have felt instinctively the beginning in contemporary science of the vindication of the ancient Asian art, which is that of storytelling. From under the banyan tree, the old master never denied his own presence. Even as he began his tale with "Once upon a time...," it was his understanding, and his listeners' own as well, that no further disclaimers or disguises were necessary.

That ancient voice was in Franz Kafka, but he was to be heard with what well might have been a new listening device, as we shall try to explain later. For now, meanwhile, there is the device called class. How it changes a reader's text is a thought we must pursue.

For an example close to home, we borrow from no less authoritative a source than William Jovanovich, the New York publisher. In his book on the art of publishing,[54] he gives us a "most remarkable (although unintentionally so) satire on editing that exists."

Consider the following from an editor's letter to a Korean writer whose manuscript appears to have been in the process of "evolving":

...Because you have been rather vague about all the

physical details of the scene, details which I am sure you have visualized in your mind but have not presented to the reader, it ends up by becoming ludicrous.

The scene belongs in the book, and is very important in clarifying the motivation. But it has an entirely uncharacteristic weakness: it is not visual. Throughout the rest of the book you present wonderful visual images which enable the American reader to see your Koreans and their land. Please don't misunderstand me. I am certainly not asking you to write an obscene chapter. Erotic, of course. Obscene, no.[55]

XII

THE letter is an explicit manual of instruction on how an artist can survive, on how to reconstitute the materials of the imagination—Fanon's "slow composition" and "definitive structuring." In short, it describes completely what our author should and should not do, how he should handle the hapless creatures of his imagination.

These happen to be youthful lovers named Sook-ja and Chul-foo. How these two must "go to a fisherman's shack to engage in their first dalliance" is the subject of the next adjuration:

> ...I don't know exactly how to make the distinction to you, but several of us here feel that it is more obscene to be vague than to be forthright. After all, this is the first sexual experience for both Sook-ja and Chul-foo, a moment of deep emotion. This has disappeared almost entirely from the scene. What are Sook-ja's feelings? This too must be added, and is perhaps *more important than anything else I have to suggest.* The way you handle the scene now, Sook-ja is almost a piece of furniture.

You should be much more frank in this scene, in a pure and lyrical and idyllic way. After all these are very young people making love for the first time. By being vague, you simply prepare the ground for a very bad reaction from your readers, since the whole setting is very challenging. No doubt this will be the first time in literature that anyone has made love in a sardine cauldron. And for reasons too complicated to explain in a letter, please call it a *cauldron* throughout, and not a *pot.*

And this is not all. You further compound the ludicrousness of the scene by confusing two appetites: hunger and sex. It simply will not do to have Sook-ja and Chul-foo eat leftover sardines out of the same cauldron in which they make love. Why shouldn't there be two cauldrons, one for each appetite? Or perhaps they could find some leftover sardines elsewhere in the shack.

Another point: You have had Chul-foo light a fire under the cauldron a little while before they begin to make love! At that point the reader doesn't think of the idyllic moment, but worries about blisters on Sook-ja's bottom. I'm sorry to be so coarse about this, but these are the reactions you arouse by vague writing. Furthermore, the fact that the shack is in darkness, and that you don't describe the banked fire very clearly, nor the kind of stove (I believe the Japanese call it a *kama-do*) being used all adds to the confusion.

It would be a great mistake to delete this scene, because it adds greatly to the structure of the book. But it must be rewritten entirely, with great care. I think you will have to provide some dim light from the fire in the shack, and give a much clearer visual description. Furthermore, you will have to prepare the reader carefully for the size of the cauldron. Unless you stress its size, the situation will seem impossible. It would help if Chul-foo failed to light a fire under the cauldron, and if it were still kept warm by the ashes underneath. Ashes retain their heat for quite a long time. Then Sook-ja could quite logically climb into the cauldron to keep warm, and Chul-foo eventually, having found sardines elsewhere, could creep in to join her.

One more detail. What kind of skirt is it that is fastened around Sook-ja's bosom? If Korean skirts do indeed fasten this way, then I think you may lay the groundwork in some detail, explaining just why Chul-foo reached for Sook-ja's bosom to unfasten her skirt. This is part of the general vagueness in physical description.

I am afraid a problem exists concerning the word *bottom*. Certainly the cauldron has a bottom, but so has Sook-ja, and no matter how you handle your description of the cauldron, readers will inevitably associate the two bottoms. I am afraid you better do without the word bottom entirely, since there are many words for both kinds of bottom...[56]

William Jovanovich's comment on the above is, no doubt, a calculated understatement: "The editing of novels," he says, "is not usually this complicated; but then, neither is love-making."

Franz Kafka was lucky—he had Max Brod. Franz Kafka saw in his manuscripts a lifework to be consigned to the fire; Max Brod saw something to be dutifully saved for posterity. At some point it was a question of which of the two was in his right mind.

Kafka's reader in the Third World today approaches the work much like the way Kafka's contemporaries did. For example, a selection of excerpts from the best 1971 editorials of the *Asia-Philippines Leader* had the following:

With the fall of Rome, the empire disintegrated into tiny feudal fragments, where government was symbolized by fences: the moat around the wall around the battlements around the hill on which stood the lord's castle—separated by water, fire, stone and steep from the governed, down in the valley.

One meaning of the castle was indeed the gap between the ruler and the ruled; but another meaning was the power, not of the mighty lord, but of those wretched peasants down in the valley. If the peasants were not feared as powerful, there would be no need for all those fences. A fence is not only to keep something in but also to keep something out.[57]

The pieces on the theme of alienation that the so-called modern reader finds today in Kafka were larger-than-life profiles of oppression in Kafka's own circle.

In the Manila of my 40s and 50s, the language situation—for one—bore a pronounced resemblance to that in Kafka's Prague. When kafka was a beginning writer in Prague, wrote Johann Bauer, the "German written and spoken... was a stiff, petrified idiom, the dialect basically of a single class."[58] This dead and prosaic language was, however, official. Slowly but surely, Bauer observed, it underwent the vivifying influence of Czech, in intonation, phraseology, and syntax.

In the Philippine case, the native-born experts in the teaching of English as a second language—products of the institutes for this sort of study, of which there are a number in the United States—know this phenomenon only too well. The English language does not escape the Tagalog syntax when spoken by the Tagalog-born, nor the felicitous Ilongo intonation of the Ilongo-born.

To continue with the Kafka case: "Literature," wrote Bauer, "was one of the fields in which, for many years, Kafka sought to link himself with the outside world, but as time went on he fell more and more out of sympathy with the German writers of his country. For relief, he turned to the Czech language, which he read and wrote fluently."

His Czech writings contain no more "mistakes" than do those of the best Czech authors. Meanwhile, his German contemporaries "either ignored their Czech fellow citizens or looked on them and their history with a detached form of romantic idealism, as a picturesque piece of national folklore or as a childlike people with the charm of youth, engaged in learning the business of life and developing a culture of their own."[59] Kafka did not identify very much, however, "with Czech national feeling," even though he maintained, a "steady" interest in the writings of his Czech contemporaries.

That the language environment in which a literary artist works becomes a determinant in his art is underscored by the information Bauer furnishes us. Enter now Max Brod, but for whom Kafka's work would not be around at all. For, in time, "Kafka found it harder and harder to make contact with the world, till finally all the roads were closed."

The silence observed by the generations of Filipino writers who began their careers in the late twenties and early thirties—and who would now only be hitting their strides, even if they had more good fortune—may well be explained by seeing their situation as analogous to Kafka's withdrawal, although not so extreme.

XIII

GENIUS has its own way. In withdrawal and alienation from the world, Kafka's genius found nourishment instead of a withering of power. By a happy coincidence, his development coincided with the growing popularity of surrealism. Bauer makes a case for this: Kafka began to be thought of in his country "as the delineator of an alien world with its own precise yet inscrutable rules, the purpose of which is apparently to discredit our own world by involving it and us in a remorseless, unintelligible conflict.[60]

Thus, we read Kafka's works today with an eye to his withdrawal and alienation instanced by language. But how did his contemporaries read him? What did they consider his purpose to be? What, according to their lights, was his subject?

Besides paying tribute to the rare quality that distinguished Kafka as a German-language writer, Jan Gremla, one of his obituarists, wrote of how "deeply" Kafka "saw the poverty of some and the power and wealth of others, and in a style full of imagination and parody launched a fierce attack on the great ones of this world."[61]

Milena Jesenska's reading of Kafka's career was similar: "He saw the world as a place full of invisible demons waiting to rend and destroy defenseless human creatures...All his books are full of the sense of hidden misunderstanding, or human beings wronging one another without blame."[62]

It is impossible to ignore the ignominious blue collar that is at the heart of Gregor Samsa's problem, structured in Kafka's mind as a metamorphosis. And for an extreme case of a bureaucracy holding up Justice as an ideal, we have his restructuring of experience as a penal colony. Yet Justice is, for good or ill, not the facet of Kafka's diamond that catches the critical light these days—however sincerely we are told by voices from his quarter that his contemporaries read him in that way. We simply do not have any Milena Jesenska or Jan Gremla with us. Their sensibilities have, for our purposes, become obsolete, their very presence incompatible with our age.

But perhaps we should say "circumstances" instead of "age." In the case of the Filipino, particularly, History has placed the writer in a bind. He can be himself or the national that he is besides. The difficulty is with "or"—which, temptingly, can also be changed to "and." In the first instance, the Filipino writer becomes committed to the subject of Alienation; in the second, to Justice. And as if writing in the stream of History were not demanding enough, he would in any case be misread or, even worse, unread.

With his society constituted as it is, he has a considerable amount of coping to do. As writer, he is the Outsider in every case—to that class in the triad to which he belongs by birth, as well as to the class he has elected to join by exigencies of education, employment, or both. It is his awareness of all these circumstances, however, that defines his relevance and meaning. He must, in short, establish and work within a dialectic provided by his art and necessary subject.

XIV

OVERLOOKING our country's place in, and our relationship with, History, we seized upon the "human condition" for our subject. I see this now as a grave error, or at the very least a waste of time and effort. But we learn, we discover. We know that the world throughout is concerned with the dismantling of colonies—the old as well as the new. Only in the most haphazard fashion have some of our writings stumbled upon this bit of comedy or that bit of tragedy connected with this tremendous operation, the stark truth involved being appreciable only as a century-long process.

Comforted by our illusions about the human condition, we joined our voices with those whom History had provided a more comfortable bed in which to suffer, a larger prison in which to languish. It is the case of the slave seeking common cause with the Master (as in *The Robe*, with Victor Mature?) and receiving ample encouragement for the effort. Look, we drag the same ball and chain, says one to the other. And especially in a borrowed tongue, communication with comforting words is not impossible. The fraternal feelings aroused can be most touching.

However, one gets preoccupied with a style of self-pity all ones's own. With the pinky, one gouges out dirt from the tiny creases of the navel, which, with its reassuring stink, is in fact the center of the world. And then how ennobling to provide, from our side, the words of assent, the commendation of an olfactory version of universal brotherhood. Our role, thus, has become that of claques of despair, whereas all the while History solicits our commitment, asking even that we go beyond and transform Justice into a passion.

"Tell us more about how it hurts!" And when you do, as when Chinua Achebe renders the agony of the crumbing of a people's culture in *Things Fall Apart*,[63] you may expect the warm endorsement of the *New York Times*. Your point will be missed. Said Achebe at the Leeds Conference of Commonwealth Literature (1964):

> Here, then, is an adequate revolution for me to espouse—to help my society regain its belief in itself and put away the complexes of the years of denigration and self-denigration.[64]

All for one end: to dignify his people, even as they suffered the traumatic processes of change. The key word is dignity, and the particularity of art somehow achieved that. To be involved in rendering dignity, then, is to be quite useless to those who desire their writers to turn into literary peons, sharecroppers of style, wordmongers.

In putting together the stories that comprise *Seven Hills Away*, I got myself caught, no doubt, in an obligation to speak from then on about Mindoro, the people of the backwoods, and about the barrio and town. Although these people might become city folk, I seem to see them at their best against the background of the life to which they eventually return.

In the mid-thirties, when those stories began to appear, only the Mountain Province folk and the farming and fishing village people of Central and Southern Luzon live in our fiction. It was the novelty of the *kaingin* as a setting for a fictional work that opened the pages of the *Philippine Magazine* to me. From that point on, I had my work to do; and having chosen fiction as my means toward this end, I found it necessary only to make the fiction as worthy of attention as possible. Which has forced me to work to the utmost of my limitations, using in freedom, and even as assets, my many disadvantages.

I only wish now that I had started the work in Tagalog (now called Filipino), which I ought to have put early at my command. But having been born into a Visayan family, an early beginning in that direction was simply not possible. I learned my Tagalog by listening to politicians deliver those interminable speeches of theirs heavy with promises. In any case, the national government was not to be bothered with a national language problem until much later.

By 1950 and after three books, I felt that language was the crucial factor in promoting a more vigorous, productive, and abundantly meaningful writing community. As writers, we were lacking in independence, to say the least. We tended to hire ourselves out; we reduced ourselves voluntarily into mere items in the job market. Our main difficulty was in our being able to address only a small audience, the so-called English-educated. It was pointed out, however, as also our greatest asset. We could not find sustenance and prevail; however, at a PEN Conference in Baguio, President Carlos Garcia urged us to relish every opportunity to starve.

Whereas we in the Philippines yearned for freedom (although we were loath to admit that we were not all that free), I saw the ambience and the elbow room available already to writers in other parts of Asia and Southeast Asia because of their use of their own languages as the media of literary expression. In a series of essays, *Sa Kabilang Dalampasigan*, published in *Liwayway*,[65] I tried to describe this yearning, this hope. A short piece in *Kislap* entitled "At Bakit Hindi?" made an appeal to common sense, urging a change of national policy concerning the expenditure of national income for an educational system conducted in a medium that was truly alien and did not work.[66] Nobody listened.

To the Tagalog-born, my position provided a mixture of amusement (*katuwa-tuwa* was the word) and satisfaction. "Look at this fellow, who, after all, is a Bisayan," etc., etc. "But he must use *our* Tagalog, not his own mixture—which is an odd cross between English and Bisayan." Thus, very early I could have made good use of a seriously edited Tagalog dictionary. But was such a book around to match my three pesos? A Funk and Wagnalls in Filipino, although usually well-stocked the Philippine Education Company had none. These were the years when, even as now, the Tagalog purists and the vernacularists were very much at odds with one another.

Nevertheless, I was to do a considerable amount of writing in Tagalog in the course of composing *The Bamboo Dancers*. That was a joy to do, a sheer joy. Between the page I was working on and the language I heard around me—and generally wherever I might happen to be, I had no classroom teaching duties then—I had a one-to-one correspondence with the world, with my surroundings. As a bus passenger, thinking of a scene for my book while en route to some place in downtown Manila, my thoughts lived, so to speak, in the same language environment as those of the people whose conversations about the weather and sundry matters I overheard.

XV

BUT all that joy was short-lived, for my editor friends had misgivings about the theme and structure of my novel. Their interest in experimenting was less than nil; they had been hired to locate reasonable gratifications for an audience whose lives, as one editorial executive explained it to me, "were too harsh already to be burdened with realism."

The accepted idea of writing was that one composed for the masses (the *pambakya* then being produced) or for the elite (*pampanitikan* material—pieces that might be considered for a literary prize). These notions seemed to have gotten a firm hold not only among the editors but throughout the publishing industry itself. Moreover, the monopolistic structure of the Tagalog publishing industry had proved that there was no need for change. Printing costs were continually rising, and there were fewer and fewer U.S. dollars available for the increased quantity of paper and ink needed to satisfy a mounting circulation. And writers are generally expendable.

I had a long and, alas, unrecorded and all-too-private discussions on this subject[67] with several people, my position being that the best the Filipino writer is capable of is never quite good enough for the Filipino masses.

But this was not acceptable. Writing meant following the conventions of the trade as practised by that class for which the industry provided profit. It did not mean pursuing the demands of an art form, and least of all the demands of an idea. It did not include the notion that characters are, like people, entitled to one's respect; nor that fictional material might lend the sort of dignity that Achebe envisions. Writing and publishing were business enterprises—not exercises in nobility or educational projects intended to inculcate high ethical values.

I was forced to return to English. Earlier, I had written *A Season of Grace*, the best text of which—I dare say—insofar as the Cebuano reader is concerned must be the Cebuano one published in *Bisaya* by Tiburcio Baguio, the translator. The English one, while agreeable to several critics, is still "not quite for us"—to use the cliche of the American publishing establishment. Two translations, however, are available: a Russian text issued by Nauka, in 1974, and the Malay, by Dewan Bahasa Dan Pustaka, in 1981.

It is sheer fantasy, then, to imagine—as some do—that I have fashioned my work to satisfy the taste of the Western literary establishment. To begin with, nobody in his right mind knows what that audience favors or needs at any one point in the publishing day. Nor would anybody in his right mind think of pitting his efforts against all comers, for these number over 3,000 writers behind that many books rolling off the presses everyday. You do what you can, in short.

And the young man with the serious look on his face, out there at the back of the room, raises his hand and asks: "How do you know that what you do is the best that you can do?" Our answer—perhaps as good as yours—calls for working in terms of integrity, validity, and accessibility. Surely these words cannot be too frightening. A reader enters a piece of writing only when it is accessible, enjoys it when its parts are valid enough to hold together, and endorses it in admiration when he realizes that its author has put something of himself on the line. For the writer, the process must work in reverse. In the end it is the work that matters.

The Bamboo Dancers, the novel that followed *Season*, had better luck in that Swallow published it in 1961. Then *SaturdayReview* hurried to give it a damning notice, which was dutifully picked up by a Creole-dominated Manila daily, the point being to demonstrate that Gonzalez was not that good. How dare he move up from the Barrio, even to America? This is easy enough to understand, and one goes to Fanon for support. Los Angeles *Times*, though, carried a very positive notice.

For all that, *Dancers* seems to be doing its work, and there is a letter somewhere in which a distinguished critic (whom I am not permitted to name here) saw to the very page and line the very navel of the book. My point here is that you might conceive your art from way out there in the boondocks and yet find a reader in some village north of Boston who will read it with enough sensitivity and recognize what you have done.

Indeed this happens. And your characters, you realize, deserve all the best wishes and good will in the world. They have become themselves, independent entities, real identities who will make friends of their own. With such a smile of fortune in store for his characters, the Filipino writer has no alternative but to be as true to his art as he possibly can.

But, again, it is sheer fantasy to believe that the world is interested in us. We can only do what we can. It does no good to be sentimental about it, but it is a fact that to this day nothing that I have written has been published anywhere else but first at home in the Philippines. All my books are native-born. Thus identified, they will have to find their way somehow. They will have to be more or less on their own. I have had to borrow tools and skills here and there, but the stories have to be told and there are yet others to come.

In "A Story Yet to be Told,"[68] I advanced the idea that what literary experience we have had so far in the Philippines can well be chalked up as exercises in preparation for some larger task. Although requested by an Australian review, the essay was also published in Manila's *Solidarity* and reprinted in the Hague.

"Please tell us more about little Porton," said a Frenchwoman who happened to read *Season of Grace* in Hong Kong in 1968. And using Tarang as a unifying character, R. Rybkin, in 1970, put together an anthology of short stories by writers in English and Tagalog as well.[69]

The list covered the period of the Philippine short story from the early thirties to the present, including Genoveva Edrosa-Matute, Fernando Samonte, Pablo N. Bautista, Jose Garcia Villa, R. Cruz, Fausto Galauran, T.D. Agcaoili, Mabini Rey Centeno, G. Guzman, Manuel Ocampo, L. Balmori, Juan T. Gatbonton, D. Paulo Dizon, Manuel E. Arguilla (although here, the Russians seem to reveal their bias for exactness by using Arguilla's middle name as well, Estabillo), Manuel Arguelles, Liwayway Arceo, F. Sionil Jose, Aida Rivera-Ford and Cornelio Reyes.

What an interesting gallery—interpreters, all of them, of the Philippine earth. It is obvious to me that Mr. Rybkin is aware that his readers are eager to learn as much as possible about us, and that isolation and cultural separateness have come to an end in this our century.

Interesting questions come to mind. Did Rybkin know where our literary beginnings lie? Did he see the influence of Turgenev? Of Chekhov? Did he see how Tarang can be envisaged by an admirer of Bunin? And concerning such a society as our stories suggest—because, despite their varying skills, I believe they offer the reader a firm structure of honesty throughout—did he see what the future holds for us?

One more item must be included here—*Reiswein Die Philippinen*, a short story anthology put together in the little

Bavarian town of Herrenalb by Horst Erdman, working in cooperation with Pura Santillan Castrence and the Bonn government's cultural institute, Internationes.[70] The collection sold well enough in Germany, for the Germans too have been eager to have an idea of how we live. And so, in sum, what does all this mean?

Quite simply, this: that perhaps through his artistic effort the Filipino can contribute to the dialog of cultures now going on all over the world.[71]

We cannot hope for too much, and yet we can do no less. We have Harold C. Conklin's word for it. Consider the *kalutang*, those two musical sticks:

> Daily food-getting and essential economic activities involve foot travel to and from swiddens, forests, streams, and neighboring settlements. Except during the rice and maize-growing season, when destructive environmental spirits might be attracted to the maturing crops, certain instruments are played while hiking.

Among these are the *kalutang*, cut from either the "bayug" (sp. *ptersospermum*) or the "danglug" (sp. *grewia*), and

> peeled, tested, and then kept or rejected...When starting out on a trail together, several *kalutang* players select their stick pairs so that the different tones produced will not "fight each other."[72]

Side 2, Band 3. I have just put the Hanunóo record on my KLH portable player. Portable—because, who knows where you will be next year? Or the year after next? To say this is to accept the fact that this is the age of travel.

For we move from swidden to swidden. From clearing to clearing. And these sticks do keep us company; they make the going more pleasant. The chance that "destructive environmental spirits" may be abroad and become attracted to our person is, of course, never remote.

At the same time, they may very well be attracted to the crop—to the "rice and maize," or whatever is soon due for harvest. To dictate to the spirits and at the same time play the *kalutang* is not possible. It is enough that solid ground, whether illusory or real, lies under our feet, and that not too far away is that next clearing, and the next, and the next...

Notes

1. William Golding, "Body and Soul," in William Golding, *The Hot Gates and Other Occasional Pieces* (New York: Harcourt, Brace & World, 1965), p. 22.
2. Writers of my generation in Malaya and Singapore had not been as fortunate. See my "The Artist in Southeast Asia," *Books Abroad*, Autumn 1956, pp. 387-91.
3. See: Ivan D. Illich, *Celebration of Awareness: A Call for Institutional Revolution* (New York: Doubleday, 1970), pp. 39-55.
4. Pierre Jalee, *The Pillage of the Third World*, trans. Mary Klopper (New York: Monthly Review Press, 1968), p. 2.
5. David Caute, *Frantz Fanon* (New York: Viking Press, 1970).
6. Jean-Paul Sartre, "Introduction" to Frantz Fanon, *The Wretched of the Earth* (New York: Grove Press, 1968), p. 8.
7. *Ibid.*
8. Quoted in Irving Louis Horowitz, *Three Worlds of Development, The Theory and Practice of International Stratification* (New York: Oxford University Press, 1972), p. 101.
9. See: Alden Cutshall, *The Philippines: Nations of Islands* (Princeton, N.J.: Van Nostrand, 1946), pp. 106-07.
10. Carlos P. Romulo, *I Walked with Heroes* (New York: Holt, Rinehart and Winston, 1961).
11. See *Philippines Free Press* 35, no. LXII (20 August 1969).
12. *Ibid.*, p. 153.
13. *Ibid.*, p. 158.
14. For the equivalent phenomenon in Latin America, see Illich, *Celebration of Awareness*, pp. 93-111. The idea of education as "bridge" is in fact Father Illich's insofar as it is understood as "schooling" or the "school system"—which, he says, "restricts all unconventional crossings and leaves the underachiever to bear the blame for his marginality."
15. John Kenneth Galbraith, "An Introduction to India," *Travel and*

Leisure 2, No. 3 (June-July 1972): 38.

16. *Ibid.*, p. 39.
17. Octavio Paz, *The Labyrinth of Solitude* (New York: Grove Press, 1961).
18. *Ibid.*, p. 11.
19. Michael Glenny, "Alexander Solzhenitysyn and the Epic Tradition," *Harper's*, August 1972, p. 52.
20. Horowitz, *Three Worlds of Development*, pp. 72-113.
21. Frantz Fanon, *Black Skin, White Masks*, trans. Charles Lam Markmann (New York: Grove Press, 1967), p. 18.
22. *Ibid.*
23. *Ibid.*
24. There is a letter somewhere in which Jose Garcia Villa, writing from self-exile in New york, commends warmly the story "Pioneer," one of the pieces I refer to. Critical benedictions of this kind did both good and harm.
25. Fanon, *Black Skin, White Masks*, p. 10.
26. *Ibid.*, pp. 110-11.
27. Illich, *Celebration of Awareness*, pp. 95-111.
28. These horse-drawn vehicles were still to be seen in postwar Manila, having bested the jeeps that were converted into mini-buses and called "jeepneys."
29. A.V.H. Hartendorp, "The Importance of Filipino Literature in English," *Philippine Magazine* vol. 34, no. 1 (January 1937): 18.
30. *Ibid.*, pp. 18-19.
31. *Ibid.*, p. 48.
32. Boston: Little, Brown and Co., 1947.
33. New York: Harcourt, Brace and World, 1944.
34. New York: Avon, 1957.
35. See O'Brien's enthusiastic Introduction to Villa's stories in Jose Garcia Villa, *Footnote to Youth* (New York: Scribner's, 1933).
36. New York: Farrer, Straus and Cudahy, 1960.
37. David Caute, *The Illusion* (New York: Harper & Row, 1972).
38. New York: Viking, 1942.
39. *London Times Literary Supplement*, 5 May 1972, p. 562.
40. See n. 30, Mr. Hartendorp himself could not but call up the occasion.
41. Fanon, *Black Sin, White Masks*, p. 38.
42. *Ibid.*, p. 39.
43. Alfred Kazin, "Displaced Person," *New York Review of Books*, 30 December 1971, p. 3.
44. John Updike, "Out of the Glum Continent," *New Yorker*, 13

November 1971, pp. 187-204.

45. *Ibid.*

46. See S.E. Solberg, "The Pinoy as Writer," *Solidarity* VI, no. 9 (September 1971): 27.

47. For Carunungan, see n. 33 and for Javellana, n. 32; Nolledo's work was published in New York by Dutton in 1970.

48. Miguel Bernad, *Bamboo and the Greenwood Tree: Essays on Filipino Literature in English* (Manila: Bookmark, 1961), pp. 100-08.

49. James Thurber, *The Years with Ross* (Boston: Little Brown, 1959), p. 226.

50. V.S. Pritchett, "Late Starter," *New York Review of Books,* 23 March 1972.

51. *Ibid.* In connection with Pritchett's mention of the Russian tradition, see the remarks by Hartendorp to which we refer in n. 30.

52. *Ibid.*

53. See Wylie Sypher, *Literature and Technology, The Alien Vision* (New York: Random House, 1968), pp. 127-35.

54. William Jovanovich, *Now, Barabas* (New York: Harcourt, Brace, Jovanovich, 1964).

55. *Ibid.,* p. 81.

56. *Ibid.,* pp. 81-84.

57. *Asia-Philippines Leader,* 16 June 1972, p. 67.

58. Johann Bauer, *Kafka and Prague* (New York: Praeger, 1961).

59. *Ibid.,* p. 73.

60. *Ibid.,* p. 180.

61. *Ibid.,* p. 182.

62. *Ibid.,* pp 174-77.

63. London: Heineman, 1958.

64. Quoted in Adrian A. Roscoe, *Mother is Gold: A Study in West African Literature* (Cambridge: University Press, 1971).

65. 25 November 1957 to 3 March 1958.

66. 25 September 1958.

67. The magazine *Vak,* now defunct, edited by S. Vatsayan and published in New Delhi, reproduced a radio interview on the subject, but I cannot recall the date of publication.

68. *Quadrant* 68:111-15.

69. R. Rybkin, *The Children of the Soil: Short Stories by Filipino Writers* (Moscow: Foreign Languages Press, 1970).

70. Birkenfeld, Gunther, and Castrence, eds., *Reiswein Die Philippinen* (Herrenalb: Internationes, 1965).

71. Although when I asked a friend what he thought these pages

might do, he said: "Just about as much as a pebble scratching the side of the Yosemite!" And so be it, but the effort is there.

72. Harold C. Conklin, *Hanunóo Music from the Philippines*, Ethnic Folkways Library Album FE 4466, Folkways Records and Service Corp., 1955.

III

The Father and the Maid:
Essays on Filipino Life and Letters

To *Robert V. Williams*
in memory of a friendship

Preface

"Welcome home to the University!"

With these words President Jose V. Abueva, in a letter dated May 11, 1988, could not have described more meaningfully how I might spend my year as the University's first International Writer-in-Residence. The Diliman campus has been home for my family since 1950; our separation from it—from the late sixties to the mid-eighties—had been merely physical, a concession to geography. While abroad, I continued with my teaching, first at the University of California, Santa Barbara, and later at the State University of California, Hayward. There had been other brief assignments elsewhere: Hongkong, Berkeley, Los Angeles. I taught, principally, Creative Writing. "Can one teach Writing?" the question is not infrequently asked, even today. At the University of Washington, I spent a specially memorable quarter teaching Philippine History. At this point in time I had been away already eleven years. If it is possible to say that there is one particularly stressful subject to teach, it is Philippine History. Wherever one turns, the theme of betrayal raises its ugly head.

This is not the occasion, of course, for pursuing the matter; suffice it to say that was how it felt. The more I look back on that experience the greater my certainty that, for a Filipino, this is the obligatory story to tell. It occurred to me that my absence from Diliman had been a preparation for new work ahead. The President's welcome expressed a disavowal fo the claim that "you can't go home again." The truth is, one must. And one must get others to join, if one could, in what needs to be done. While writing is individual effort, private and even idiosyncratic, the activity that aspires toward a national literature is "bayanihan" commitment.With this in mind, I had every reason to make the allotted year as fruitful as possible, given the possibility of redefining a purpose and determining a new direction.

The Likhaan: Sentro ng Makathaing Pagsulat (Creative Writing Center) of the University of the Philippines generously provided its facilities for the lectures that are here reproduced. They were given during the period from November 1988 to January 1989. New materials have been added here and there; perhaps not all the murky areas have been eliminated or cleared away, but I've tried to do just that. Thanks are due Professor Amelia L. Bonifacio, Director, who exerted every effort to bring the series to the attention of faculty members, students, and guests from other colleges and universities. With considerable patience and admirable humor all throughout, she chaired the question-and-answer period that usually followed each meeting. I am also indebted to Professor Francisco Arcellana, who, in his opening remarks at the beginning of the series, introduced the lecturer by liberally drawing from his reminiscences of the mid-thirties and the forties, which was when they both started writing. It would have been difficult, in 1935, to imagine that our probes at creativity would evolve into long teaching and writing careers at the university.

To Dr. Gemino H. Abad, Vice-President for Academic Affairs, and to President Abueva and the Board of Regents—let this little volume express thanks for their confidence in the idea of engaging a writer-in-residence at the University.

Thanks are also due Rowena Concepcion and her team, who covered the meetings on behalf of the Cultural Center of the Philippines; and, once again, all the gratitude and love to my wife, Narita, for help and support beyond measure.

N.V.M. GONZALEZ

1. The Father and the Maid

In which Manuel E. Arguilla's "How My Brother Leon Brought Home a Wife" and Aida L. Rivera-Ford's "Love in the Cornhusks" provide the occasion for describing how much "lived life" in Filipino terms a story may achieve.

*I*t might strike many readers as a surprise, but it is perfectly possible to study fiction—and modern fiction, at that—by drawing texts from Philippine literature. Given the mind-set we call modern, which allows saying "more than one thing at a time to express the complexity of experience,"[1] there is the experience we call art, which fiction is; and we have been assured that artists will continue to resort to it in their "search for significance through the cultural paradoxes exposed by their perception of discrepancies"[2] that public and private events provide.

It cannot be said that the Filipino writer, considering the difficulties that abound in the exercise of his craft and art, has despaired in his efforts to mediate and assess the cultural paradoxes and discrepancies that our circumstances as a people reveal. Take the conflict between barrio and city, between country and metropolis; or the paradox of poverty amidst plenty: certainly these have not escaped our writers' attention, sketchy though our awareness of their efforts may be, owing to our unfamiliarity with their art in general.

Two short stories, one by Manuel E. Arguilla, "How My Brother Leon Brought Home a Wife," and another by Aida L. Rivera-Ford, "Love in the Cornhusks," provide the texts that we can "read" with profit in this context. Arguilla's story is perhaps one of the most widely read Filipino short stories in English. For our purposes, it may well have been written in some other language or vernacular. It is unclear to me why special reference to the medium has become a convention in classroom and critical writing. It seems that a superiority once claimed for English as a medium for literary expression has now dissipated; at best a deference to English is possible in light of a change in the cultural climate. This is unfortunate; a story is a triumph of storytelling and deserves to be regarded as such. And a triumph over what? you ask. Of the storyteller over the unformed and incoherent material we call life. In this context, the language in which that achievement is rendered becomes secondary. I cannot help recalling the excitement in Manila's small but inspired literary community when Whit Burnett published "How My Brother Leon Brought Home a Wife" in *Story Magazine*: the event was a triumph of the Filipino short story in English, it was claimed. So indeed it was; but we would think of it differently today. More than anything else, we'd say, I believe, that it was indicative of what the Filipino short story can do for the historical experience we call our being Filipino.

Arguilla certainly drew from personal history, from the Nagrebcan, in Bauang municipality, La Union Province, of his childhood and youth, and from the Ermita district, in Manila, of his young manhood. Nagrebcan is perhaps one geo-graphical actuality on Luzon that has been most artistically presented in our literature. To this day the word "charming" is often used to describe the private level that readers reach on meeting Arguilla's work, and many are happy enough with that. It gratifies the expectation of those delighted over what a glance at youthful experience might offer, a fact which many readers particularly concerned with a received language might stress. The fact is that immensely successful writing offers more than what its appears to be able to do. To merely assert that a story works for us is actually our way of admiring it into oblivion; to claim that it makes a statement is merely to associate it with some current ideology. Thus we manage to overlook almost entirely what a writer does, when he does succeed, which is to express the ineffable.

Think back on how in this sense, readers have failed Faulkner's "A Rose for Emily" and Hemingway's "Hills Like White Elephants"—to cite two stories popular with undergraduates and their mentors. In the first, it is the macabre that attracts them; in the second, the issue of abortion. Having vicariously indulged both topics, readers feel that they have done well enough by the authors. Neither Faulkner's insight on Time nor Hemingway's on the nature of romantic illusions comes into the readers' field of vision. Frank O' Connor would only limit himself to calling our attention, in the case of the Hemingway story, to "the repetition of key words and phrases," hence the hypnotic effect, "a new thing in story telling...." This notion is well enough learned; but a less trained reader, having been told that much, is likely to persevere no further. This is not unlike discovering the "charm" in Arguilla.

In any event, let us consider the materials Arguilla used and what he did with them. He gave us oppositions like "city" and "country," "father" and "sons," "Maria (an import from the city)" and "Leon (an export from the country)," "the bed of the Waig" and "the provincial road," "the sky full of stars" and "the land that has experienced a revolution," etc., etc. The alert reader soon recognizes the pattern of return that the writer has designed for Leon, as well as for his opposite, Baldo. Unlike Leon, who will need the actuality of the bed of the Waig, Baldo requires a fictive or imagined ground.

His point of departure is an area of innocence, his point of arrival that of awareness. For Arguilla gives us two journeys in opposition: one, in terms of space, is the return to home; the other, in terms of time, generational time, not to a place but to a history and tradition.

Units of clock and calendar time lie between the recovery of the journey of return through memory and its transformation into narrative. These two become Baldo's time, which also become the reader's, since it is Baldo's story that the latter follows. The composite is not unlike the time all of us use when moving from a condition of not knowing to that of knowing, from any one point of innocence to one of knowledge. Likewise this kind of time is the one the brothers share with their father, who, earlier, shared it with his forebears: a time rendered as a generational journey, in short. In the story's structure, is equated with the journey in space, from the city to Nagrebcan.

These oppositions have to be controlled, of course; and Arguilla does this through Baldo. It is Baldo's experience we are reading about; it is his journey that we have been following. To share in Baldo's discovery of arrival is to experience the unexpressed, this ineffable experience in space-time. Because we have been with Baldo all along, we cannot miss this, although we may not be aware of it. In any case, we first experience Baldo's emerging awareness while as yet not sentient like our own, and then the latter condition is transformed to a kind of understanding, the addition of Baldo's consciousness to our own. This sum is what the ineffable seems to be made of.

In retrospect we, as readers, simply identify it as a sense of the richness of the story. We call it charm, in an attempt to account for our having succumbed to Baldo's earnestness and his naive movement from his feelings as a young brother to those of a son of their father. Our attention to all this, in the end, is what raises Arguilla's work to the level of artistry.

We can now risk giving the story a more detailed reading. Summaries are never adequate; invariably they falsify. To render the narrative in expository form is a violence to the original, and this is unforgivable, especially if by story we mean the totality that the author has provided for us and not merely those shell shards and driftwood, like characterization, plot, atmosphere, and the like that have been washed up our critical shore and, as found objects, made into gizmos for the trade.

Baldo, as we know, has been dispatched by his father, a shrewd old man, a veteran of the Philippine Revolution of 1989, to escort home a new member of the family—a city girl,

Maria, whom Baldo's elder brother, Leon, has recently married. In Baldo's eyes, she's quite a beauty:

> She stepped down the carretela of Ca Celin with a quick, delicate grace. She was lovely. She was tall. She looked up to my brother with a smile, and her forehead was on a level with his mouth.
>
> "You are Baldo," she said and placed her hand lightly on my shoulder. Her nails were long, but they were not painted. She was fragrant like a morning when papayas are in bloom. And a small dimple appeared momently high up on her right cheek.

Anxious to see how his daughter-in-law might regard country life, the father instructs Baldo not to use the family calesa but the two-wheeled cart instead. Baldo is to hitch the bull, Labang, to the cart; and he is to return home by way of the river-bed trail instead of the provincial road. Leon sees his father's meaning clearly enough: to a city girl, the riverbed trial can be an ordeal. But Leon and his bride make a marvelous journey of it, what with the stars in the sky that night and a song that appropriately comes to mind. When Baldo delivers the couple safely home, their father asks, "Did you meet anybody on the way?" and the boy's reply, which is in the negative, is supplemented by an important bit of information: "Nobody passes through the Waig at night." Arguilla, thus, has set off from the mundane the new world to which Maria is being handed over.

The father pursues the matter further, asking whether Maria showed fear of Labang. To this Baldo replies:

> "No, Father, she was not afraid."
> "On the way—"
> "She looked at the stars, Father. And Manong Leon sang."
> "What did he sing?"
> "'Sky Sown with Stars'. She sang with him."

The father did not expect this much information, for that matter. For his part, Baldo does not grasp its importance. He does note that the father became silent at this point.

I could hear the low voices of Mother, and my sister Aurelia downstairs. There was also the voice of my brother Leon, and I thought that Father's voice must have been like that when he was young.

The connection between father, the sons, and the rest of the family with the stars has now been established. Towards the close of the story, the father reminds Baldo that it is "time you watered him (Labang), my son," and then we see the boy looking at Maria again. He knows by now that the father has been testing him. The old man has a wound acquired during the Revolution; it still festers, we remember. How Maria will impress him, city girl that she is, is not exactly predictable. Not unguardedly Baldo tells us how Leon asked Maria:

"Does that worry you still, Maria?....From the way you talk he might be an ogre for all the world...."

For perhaps Leon has been over-confident in believing that his family will accept Maria wholeheartedly. We feel, though, that nothing untoward will happen, for Baldo has told us about their singing "Sky Sown with Stars." He remembers that before Leon went to the city to study, he and their father used to sing that song while in the fields at night.

The song is now established as a bond, and a strong one, between the father and his sons. The fact is no mere romantic detail, no accident of recall. For what Arguilla is now saying is that in song the generations have a bond, that although country and city may be in opposition, and in fact are a cause of separation, a reunion is assured through song. The idea is mediated through Baldo, and in this way the author has distanced himself. We have trusted Baldo all along anyhow. He has won us to his view, although we have not become conscious of this until now. How did this happen?

The answer is in Arguilla's handling of time. We feel that no lag exists between Leon and Maria's journey and Baldo's rendering of it. Baldo's impressions have an utter freshness to them: they have not quite become memory—which, normally, they should have been transformed into. Consider the immediacy in the following:

> Now the shadows took fright and did not crowd so near. Clumps of andadasi and arrais flashed into view and quickly disappeared as we passed by. Ahead, the elongated shadow of Labang bobbed up and down and swayed drunkenly from side to side, for the lantern rocked jerkily with the cart.

The strategy is typical, and it is an example of how space, in Arguilla, has not yet become Time in concrete form.[3] It is Baldo's act of remembering that is the event being narrated here, rather than the evocation of a memory. We participate in the exercise of his virgin powers of observation rather than in the recovery of passively acquired data adulterated during the process of recall. It is difficult to say whether Arguilla did this on purpose, but that is an irrelevancy, considering that he has, in any event, managed it well.

The method works not only in the exposition of space but also in that of emotions (concerning Nature and the family, for example) and our assent to them; furthermore, it is not directly solicited. To accept Baldo completely, the author seems to say, is to accept the story's theme as well. Baldo becomes, in fact, the author in disguise. Besides providing us with a narrative, Arguilla leaves us with instructional material related to the business of living, using indirection through incident and character. The author, as Jean Paul Sartre might put it, has borrowed our innocence and tried it for size on Baldo.[4] Thus, he has also borrowed our own boyhood, as well as our own young manhood and our fatherhood, mediating for us the question of how, thanks to a wound in the leg, generations may be joined in a history and culture.

With "Love in the Cornhusks" the identification of opposites is a good starting point, too, but we probably need the strategy no longer. Better perhaps that we proceed directly with how the story goes about its business of defining love in our plantation society just as "How My Brother Leon Brought Home a Wife" went about the bonds that hold our generations together.

What we have in "Love..." is a seemingly straightforward account of a young wife and mother, Tinang, who, taking along her baby boy, visits her former mistress. The family owns what appears to be a fairly large farm; it boasts a tractor.

We learn that some time back Tinang married a Bagobo and for that reason left the family's service. A Bagobo is a non-Christian; and Bagobito is how Tinang calls their child. She has in fact come to arrange to have the baby baptized, with her former mistress for sponsor.

There is a letter waiting for her, she is told, at the local drugstore, which doubles as a post office in these parts. The letter turns out to be that of Amado, the young man who used to drive the tractor and who stopped working at the farm so as to return home to look after his ailing mother.

In rather picturesque language, Amado expresses his feelings for Tinang who, incidentally, has reached Sixth Grade. She succumbs, in fact, to memories of their friendship; her love for Amado is momentarily reawakened, more so with the little Bagobito at her side. So as to be able to read Amado's letter, Tinang puts the baby down on a bed of cornhusks. Minutes later she sees "a little green snake" slither away into the tall grass nearby. Tinang is startled remembering her child. "Ave Maria Santisima....Do not punish me," she prays, grabbing her child and hugging him close. She searches the baby's skin for possible snake bites; among the cornhusks Amado's letter lies unnoticed.

As with all summaries, we've done some violence here, although an unavoidable one. Plot usually survives this;

characterization hardly. Milieu and atmosphere is of course beyond replication in any manner. When arrived at under these handicaps, meaning becomes even less than a calculated guess.

It has been said that classics are books that continue to engage our attention; we keep caring about them through the years. With books of this kind, our good fortune is like that of a traveller in possession of travel papers that allow him to discover a country again and again without having to apply for a visa covering each visit. The critical reader is likewise provided. He holds a passport that has been stamped with multiple visas for unlimited sojourn in the countries of his choice.

What transpires during such visits? What happens after a second or third reading, in other words? With reference to our visit at this farm, what do we find objectified in the form of Tinang's love and accommodation to her circumstances? What lies beyond that stereotypical snake?

These questions, and many others, force us to return to Tinang and observe how the author has portrayed her. The dogs at the farmstead are instantly hostile to her, we note. Tinang adjusts the baby's cap upon arrival at the gate. With the exception of the little black mongrel, the entire pack rejects her.

The mongrel is called Bantay, which is Bisayan for "sentry." Obviously, the mistress's place is worth guarding. Is this a citadel or some such redoubt? What is so valuable here that there has to be a *bantay* on duty? Has this place custody of certain values in contemporary society? "The big animals barked in displeasure," Tinang observes. So, then, there are "big" dogs as well as "small," each one probably assigned specific responsibilities.

The Señora's son, Tito, is "young master" to Tinang. Although it has been some time since her last days of service in the household, she regards the boy with undiminished deference. Tinang has experienced a loss of status, for the Señora's servant has become the Bagobo's wife. To the son,

Tinang has been likewise reduced in stature. In the Señora's attitude toward her, we note censure; in the son's, malice. Fortunately, we cannot overlook Tinang's remark about how "tall" Tito has become; and so we say to ourselves, let Mother and son think that the Bagobito is a "monstrosity." True, the ears are "huge," as Tito says. Let the Señora observe that Tinang has begun to "look like a Bagobo" herself....The Señora's tone leaves us in no doubt about how low Tinang has indeed fallen.

All the more remarkable, then, that Tinang feels "a warmness" toward both the Señora and Tito. Indeed, she now sees the household, being no longer in service there, in a different light. The wisps of cologne blending with kitchen smells become the objective correlative for the comfortable world that Tinang has turned her back on to become wife to Inggo, the foul-smelling Bagobo, and mother to his child.

Noticing that Tinang is pregnant, the Señora raises a warning. "*Hala!*" she says. Or, in other words: "You had better watch out!" And to bait her into further self-awareness, the Señora makes her an offer of hand-me-downs. But she holds up pretty well under all this strain.

Why? Because Tinang is incorrigibly innocent. She makes us uncomfortable over her being still concerned about the household and the farm. In plantation society, a Señora rules through a peculiar partnership and power-sharing with a Señor. Thus, Amado, the tractor driver, is to the Señor what Tinang is to the Señora. But Amado has quit, we learn, leaving the tractor in bad repair. So has Tinang, in order to be able to join her Bagobo; she leaves the orchids for some other girl servant to look after. The Bagobo is to Tinang what Amado is to his sick mother. Bagobito's birth is to Tinang's decision to marry her Bagobo man what the mother's death is to Amado's returning home.

Now come those cries of Bagobito and the explanation that the child must be hungry. But what could be hidden here by way of meaning? The paragraphs that follow hint at an answer: once Tinang's child is baptized, Amado may become

Bagobito's model. Tinang does not say so, but we feel that some such possibility is in her mind. Tinang has had her experience of the good life, although only through her being a servant; she knows that by having Bagobito christened, and with a *madrina* for surrogate mother, that good life may be also theirs to live. But we, as readers, know better. The truth is that *madrinas* and *padrinos* are, in plantation society, principally bestowers of mere trickles of good to the lower orders; in religious matters their participation is, as likely as not, pro forma.

A collective consciousness seems, in fact, to have become operative in the child; in his own way he mounts a protest over the state of affairs into which he was born. His cry, if ostensibly indicative of hunger or some discomfort, might just as well have been an innocent's protest over the patron-worker relationship—an experience already in his blood, so to speak, since he has suckled all the while at Tinang's breast. In other words, he has already begun to endure what his mother has gone through.

Why should the Señora admit having been tempted to read Amado's letter? "To see if there was bad news," we are told. And why more warning by those dogs? Tito's restraining hands keep Tinang from being attacked by one in particular; and it is at this point that she is to learn soon about Amado's love for her. Yet the young man mounts his own "attack" by reminding her of past favors and unfulfilled obligations: "Bring me," he says, "some young corn next time."

It is at the drugstore that Tinang regains her full stature as a person. Here she ceases to be Tinang but is Constantina Tirol, and, to the disappointment of the drugstore owner, she escapes his tradesmanly power: she has not come to make a purchase but to demand that some service be rendered her. She wants her letter. She, furthermore, dispels the drugstore owner's belief that she is illiterate. In Tinang, then, Aida Rivera-Ford has created, using Nature and Society for background, a woman with at least a sense of self. It is not for nothing that the baby and the letter both are "smeared with mud," nor that Amado's letter is in English, a detail relevant to a history (personally for Amado, and publicly for national culture). Tinang may be ill-equipped to understand the implication of the letter, but a portrait of Amado emerges from its unorthodox vocabulary and syntax. Memorable details of her past as a servant at the farm overwhelm Tinang at this juncture. It seems only fitting that it was on being sent on an errand involving working tools and bolts that she and Amado should discover their love and seek to translate this knowledge in action.

There is in Tinang's mind, we now realize, a singleness of import behind the emotion she identifies as love. A woman marries the man she loves; he is her model of good. In Tinang's terms, this means being well-dressed like the local schoolteacher and being the kind of person one would consider possibly able some day to go to engineering school. To Tinang the good is the present and the future encompassed by love. This notion does not accommodate separation. This could take the form of being wife to another man, and this is hardly a promising prospect in itself. We remember that Tinang "laughed when a Bagobo with two hectares of land asked her to marry him," yet she did not remain true to her values. Two hectares of land and the Bogobo seemed preferable to silence and separation. What vitiates Tinang's perception of her future?

Certainly Amado's absence of two years has something to do with this, especially since he had planned being away for only two days. It is "now" rather than "tomorrow" that Tinang opts for. And has work at the Señora's household influenced her perception of time? Amado's seems to have been unaffected by his work as a tractor driver. He thinks in terms of long relationships; in his letter he says, "I close with best wishes to you my friends Bonding, Serafin, Bondio, etc." There is a remarkable lack of anxiety or urgency in the tone. Amado lives in a time-frame consisting of a long present and an indefinite future. Tinang's time-frame is a different one; she transforms the present readily into a past: she laughs at the Bagobo with two hectares of land and then marries him. Now, besides being her first-born, her Bagobito will also become a baptized Christian, a transformation of considerable value in plantation society. Tinang has to plan on it so as to offset her loss in love.

It seems now only appropriate that the little green snake draws an "Ave Maria Santisima!" and a prayer that she be spared punishment for her having indulged in romantic recollections in the face of the reality of her being a Bagobo's wife. This extravagant anxiety has its match in Amado's own case, his extended stay at his mother's side being a devotion of the same quality.

And are not those angry dogs yet another hyperbole? For why should they be hostile to Tinang and her child at the gate? Is not the author perhaps calling our attention to something excessive in the nature of the relationship between master and servant in this setting? This relationship has grown beyond limits through the workings of loyalties developed by institutions like marriage and the family and, ironically at that, under the aegis of Christian conventions.

Thus we have a metaphor here of love in plantation society, with death (that of Amado's mother), separation (Tinang's distance from Amado) and accommodation (Tinang's choice of the Bagobo for husband) for parameters. Tinang's present-oriented perceptions tell us that death, separation, and accommodation are all containable: we carry on, in short. The spoiled sibling of plantation culture (Tito) may grow up all the taller and demand propitiatory gifts (young corn) from stragglers (like Tinang and the baby) or some such folk as might turn up at the gate. But this is all part of the reality.

As a matter of fact, it is a reality not without a remarkable repertoire of possibilities. In Mr. Jacinto, the schoolteacher, is represented a desirable ideal and one which an Amado might emulate. The Bagobo is Mr. Jacinto's opposite; he is hardly an ideal as a husband and is only acceptable up to a point. The Señor, the Señora, and Tito are three of a kind: a triad that is the source of the day-to-day pressures characteristic of a pervasive plantation culture. Tinang and Bagobito are a duo, the baby an obvious opposite of Tito, and Tinang the embodiment of love lived out in the plantation culture.

"Come," Amado once said to Tinang, and she followed him to the "screen of trees beyond," her loyalty to the Bagobo being yet subject to a later test. That she has failed with Amado must be accepted, even as she needs yet to know what a wife's love could be like; and after this, a mother's love as well. Tinang adjusts the cap on Bagobito's head for good reason; it is only one of many adjustments to be made.

At this point, the story is ready to accept what we may wish to contribute to it. Our gift of meaning may be prefigured by those obstreperous dogs and the broken-down tractor, but there is the possibility that through a generosity available within the parameters that we know, we cannot overindulge this notoriously decrepit society. Criticism cannot dictate, however; it can only suggest areas to visit and explore. When there are no guidebooks, we may improvise itineraries and wander about on our own.

Notes

1. Tom Tashiro, "Ambiguity as Aesthetic Principle," in *Dictionary of the History of Ideas* (New York: Scribner's, 1968), p. 59.
2. *Ibid.*, p. 60.
3. Gaston Bachelard, *The Poetics of Space* (Boston: Beacon Press, 1969), p. 9. Bachelard has a name for the space which contains time: "When we dream of the house we were born in the poet well knows that the house holds childhood motionless in its arms," quoting thereafter Rainer Maria Rilke:

   > House, patch of meadow, oh evening light
   > Suddenly you acquire an almost human face
   > You are very near us, embracing and embraced.

   "At times," he continues, "we know ourselves in time, when

all we know is a sequence of fixations in the spaces of the being's stability—a being who does not want to melt away, and who, even in the past, when he sets out in search of things past, even time to 'suspend' its flight. In its countless alveoli space contains compressed time. This is what space is for."

4. John Paul Sartre, *What is Literature?* Translated by Bernard Frechtman (New York: Washington Square Press, Inc., 1966), p. 28. In the chapter "Why Write?" Sartre remarks on the substance that a "literary object" possesses as none other than "the reader's subjectivity. Raskolnikov's waiting is my waiting which I lend him. Without this impatience of the reader he would remain only a collection of signs. His hatred of the police magistrate who questions him is my hatred which has been solicited and wheedled out of me by signs, and the police magistrate himself would not exist without the hatred I have for him via Raskolnikov. That is what animates him, it is his very flesh."

2. The Road from Porto-Vecchio

In which the role of the narrator is described and why his contribution to the art of storytelling may not be taken for granted. To rescue him from the marginal role that has been traditionally given him, we begin with Prosper Mérimée's "Mateo Falcone" and move on.

To tell a story we need a storyteller; and what he needs thereafter is an audience. This triad is the be-all and end-all of narrative.

To the extent that we are under the storyteller's spell we entrust ourselves to him; and precisely because that trust is central, indeed crucial, to the pleasures of fiction, writers have mustered into service a variety of narrators, disguising them when necessary or directly engaging them for credence's sake. The narrator is there so that someone is around to tell the story.

Which may well be true, but this is not all there is to it. For it might well be that the narrator, instead of the story he has been charged to tell his audience, is in fact the story itself. Prosper Mérimée's "Mateo Falcone" is a case in point. What happens in the story is so stark we overlook how it is told. Several generations of students have read "Mateo Falcone" as palmists do the lines of the palm. They see a realism which is not easily matched. Invariably, readers forget the narrator, the events rendered having been completely absorbing. It is from what readers are told that a meaning of the story takes hold of them, and that experience is enough.

"Coming out of Porto-Vecchio, and turning northwest toward the interior of the island, the ground rises somewhat rapidly..."[1] Thus Prosper Mérimée begins his now classic story about a man who lived beyond the pale, acting out "an

115

ancient, unchanging code of honor." This code is violated by his only son, whereupon a "swift, terrible, inexorable" kind of justice descends upon the boy.

Prosper Mérimée was born in 1803, began publishing when he was 26 and wrote on till he was 40. He belonged to a school of realism that had its roots in medieval times. In a reaction to "normalism," a doctrine which held that ideas were merely names and abstractions, 13th century scholastics propounded a belief in the "reality of ideas." Thereafter the term went through considerable change in use and meaning.

Eighteenth century writers took it as the opposite of "idealism." Before the third decade of that century, the French would speak of "the literature of the true," using the term "realism" this time as the equivalent of "materialism."

It was associated with local color, costume and like paraphernalia, all of which found their way into Scott and Hugo. To this Balzac added the portrayal of manners even as a literary creed emerged in support of representations of "the real world." Its advocates asked that writers render life and manners "dispassionately, impersonally, objectively."[2]

This is Rene Wellek's synoptic account of the term. The movement it ushered included Stendhal, Balzac and Mérimée. Although Flaubert became later associated with the school, he was annoyed by the word. Wellek does not say how Flaubert responded to the enemies of realism, how he went instead for the "excessive use of minute external detail" as well as the "impersonality and objectivity" which covered up "cynicism and immorality." It was ironic, in any case, that when in 1857 Flaubert was haled into court for *Madame Bovary*, the term had been, in Wellek's estimation, "completely established in France."[3]

In another context, Wellek tells us about Mérimée's contribution to realism. As the movement won adherents, specific refinements in the practice found favor with various writers and critics. Ferdinand Brunetiere, for example, felt strongly about "moment." To him it superseded "milieu" and "race"; in the debate then current concerning the evolution of genres, he held out for them as if they were a "biological" reality.

What this means concerns us because writers like to take up positions in connection with causes that do not lack, as in this instance, for contentious and passionate votaries. To Wellek, what Mérimée got passionate about in the representation of reality was "chronology." And this must have been quite an issue: Mérimée took chronology for "king," as indeed seemed appropriate to the author of a chronicle of Charles IV's regime. A contemporary called that work "the culmination point of the French historical novel." In contrast, the other works that followed, notably Victor Hugo's *Notre Dame de Paris*, offered only samples of "slow decadence."[4]

So much for background to the work and intentions of the author of "Mateo Falcone," for all this information could seem arcane and obtuse. The story provides us with weather-beaten particulars: a high plateau in Corsica which, the narrator tells us, he visited in 18—. The tone may well have been that of Ivan Turgenev's *A Sportsman's Notebook* (1825). But it has a quality quite unlike that of Turgenev's country gentleman. Mérimée's narrator is well-born all right, but the sporting life does not interest him as much as freedom and justice do.

The narrator describes the characteristic vegetation in this section of Corsica; the maquis, which would be equivalent to the chaparral in American westerns, appears to be quite hospitable to those who, the narrator says, "wish to escape the police." Mérimée's contemporary, Ferdinand Brunetiere, would have been hard put to place the maquis on his scale of critical values:

> I would have you understand that the Corsican peasant sets fire to a stretch of woodland to save himself the trouble of manuring his fields. If the flames spread further than they should, so much the worse. In any case, he is sure of a crop if he sows on this ground, which has been fertilized by the ashes of the trees which grew on it. When the corn

has been harvested, they leave the straw, because it takes too much time to gather it up. The roots of the burned trees, which have been left in the ground un-damaged, put forth very thick shoots in the following spring, and these shoots, before many years, attain a height of seven or eight feet. It is this sort of under-growth which is called a maquis. It is composed of all sorts of trees and shrubs mingled and tangled every which way. A man has to hew his way through with an axe, and there are maquis so thick and tangled that even wild rams cannot penetrate them.

Which might well have been mere landscaping, the milieu Ferdinand Brunetiere also valued. To be sure, this place that had become home to shepherds and peasants deserves to be painted in. But isn't there better detail?

Oh yes, there is one. Time, although one that is not that of the clock, nor even that of the calendar. The moment belongs to Man's return to Nature in order to escape the stresses of civilized society, so-called. Those wild rams and the tangled growths belong to that ever so much earlier age. In Mérimée's pursuit of chronology, he has made his milieu the moment as well.

More is sketched in; we get a close-up of Mateo Falcone the man. He is a "small, sturdy man," now 50, "a good friend but a dangerous enemy," very quick with the gun, as all his neighbors know. How he wins himself a wife, raises three daughters and a son is related with great economy:

> The girls were married off satisfactorily. In a pinch their father could count on the daggers and rifles of his sons-in-law. The son was only ten years old, but already gave promise for the future.

What happens to the boy Fortunato, when one day in autumn Mateo and his wife leave to tend their flocks in a clearing on the maquis, provides the action. The boy wants to go with the father to the maquis but is not allowed to; and concerning this the narrator puts in a comment without even so much as a blush: he tells us outright that we shall see why the father is "sorry for this afterwards."

For on this fateful day Fortunato violates the code his father has lived by. As his father's son and heir, his legitimacy is tested when a wounded outlaw finds his way to the Falcone place with gendarmes in hot pursuit. Mérimée's handling of the episode is one of the greatest achievements in the short story. It is perhaps only excelled by the story's own climax and denouement.

> "Woman... Is this a child of mine?" Mateo Falcone asks his wife Giuseppa, upon discovering what Fortunato has done.
>
> Giuseppa's brown cheeks flushed brick red.
>
> "What are you saying, Mateo? Do you realize to whom you are speaking?"
>
> "Yes, perfectly well. This child is the first traitor in my family."
>
> Fortunato redoubled his sobs and choking, and Falcone kept watching him like a hawk. At last he struck the ground with the butt of his rifle, then flung it across his shoulder, returned to the path which led toward the maquis and commanded Fortunato to follow him. The child obeyed.
>
> Giuseppa ran after Mateo and clutched his arm.
>
> "He is your son," she said in a trembling voice, fixing her dark eyes on those of her husband, as if to read all that was passing in his soul.

Those last eleven words cannot pass muster these days, given our grammar and syntax of sensibilities. The forthrightness is embarrassing, but the reader is too gripped by the drama to really bother. Giuseppa has kissed her son and gone back into the house, where she flings herself on her knees before the family altar and prays fervently. Outside, Falcone walks about two hundred paces along the path to the ravine, stopping at that point to test the ground with the butt of his rifle. He finds the soil soft; it is exactly what he wants.

We cannot pursue this paraphrase further without doing great damage to the masterpiece. Enough that Abraham. H. Lass and Leonard Kriegel, from whose anthology, *Masters of the Short Story*, we have drawn this text, attribute to it "an archaic, Homeric dignity..." able to reach our "deepest emotions." The anthology appears to indicate that the story is that of Mateo Falcone, that it "belongs" to him, as we say.

But is this really so? A text must find "its fulfillment only in reading," Sartre reminds us,

> ...since the artist must entrust to another the job of carrying out what he has begun, since it is only through the consciousness of the reader that he can regard himself as essential to his work, all literary work is an appeal. To write is to make an appeal to the reader that he lead into objective existence the revelation which I have undertaken by means of language.[5]

Hence the reader must raise the question: is this Mateo Falcone's story?

The text, we realize, does not get down to the business of introducing the central character until after the first two paragraphs. The first begins with our coming out of Porto-Vecchio and turning northwest into the interior of the island; then it talks of paths, rocky boulders, and little ravines. The ravines are particularly fetching; we meet one again at the end of the story. Furthermore, we are told, in the second paragraph, about how expedient your escape to the maquis can be, "if you have killed a man," etc.

Suppose, then, that these two paragraphs serve as platform from which to mount the story, so to speak; or, suppose we take them for some sort of frame, what meaning is intended? Perhaps we have two paragraphs too many!

But contraptions have no place in a well-made tale. There must be some purpose here to be discovered, we tell ourself. Later comes the stark drama, along with an authorial reminder or two. There is one which says, "We shall see that he (Falcone) was sorry for this afterwards." The other is about Giuseppa, at the point when she is "as if (about) to read all that was passing in his (Falcone's) soul."

These reminders are superfluous. We know too well the "moment" which, on one hand, the story tries to dramatize— namely, the discovery of Fortunato's betrayal of the Falcone code and the consequences, thereof; and, on the other hand, the hint of a larger story implied in the dialog, towards the very end. The reader is only too anxious to bring the whole drama to the "revelation" of what Sartre calls an "objective existence." The author has sounded the appeal to the reader to use his freedom in collaborating with the text.

> He (Falcone) had only gone a few steps along the path when he met Giuseppa, running, for she had been alarmed by the rifle shot.
> "What have you done?" she cried.
> "Justice!"
> "Where is he?"
> "In the ravine. I am going to bury him. He died a Christian. I shall have a Mass said for him. Send word to my son-in-law, Tiodoro Bianchi, that he is to come and live with us."

Here, then, is Justice. But whose Justice? Mateo Falcone's? Ours? From what Falcone has acted out, we know definitely what he means by the word. But we have a meaning of our own as well. This meaning we share with the narrator, since he belongs, after all, to our world, not to Mateo Falcone's. To our society, not to that where the road from Porto-Vecchio goes.

You start from Porto-Vecchio, the narrator says, and go into these areas where people live beyond the pale. Out there is a country of outlaws. Ours is an orderly society and, in contrast theirs is not—although perhaps there's another kind of order out there. Take the case of Mateo Falcone...

Is this Prosper Mérimée speaking? It doesn't appear to be

so. For we can identify the narrator readily enough: the writer has made him address us directly, in the first person. It is through the narrator's eyes that we see a social order against the larger "moment" in the history of civilized society; and we allow the first-person narrator as a witness presenting an illustrative material concerning honor and justice. The setting is one where we least expect to be given the opportunity to indulge in ideals like honor and justice. Yet here is an exemplary case to consider, says the first-person narrator.

In this light we become acquainted not only with Falcone's fateful deed, brutally memorable though that may be, but also with a response to the appeal of the text that we put ourselves in mind of the norms of honor and justice in our own society. In so doing we come up with this larger story, cheek by jowl, as it were, upon the narrated one. We have brought into existence what the author has disclosed by employing a narrator.[6]

As a matter of fact, we could not have avoided collaborating in this way, having been moved by Falcone's deed. "The error of realism," Sartre says, "has been to believe that the real reveals itself to contemplation..." We are spared the stasis arising from the real, which contemplation may produce, the narrating voice being responsible for our making the comparison.[7]

The storyteller, then, has become the story itself. And it is a transformation not exactly unusual in modern literature, we realize, for we encounter it in the novels of Mihail Lermontov, Joseph Conrad, James Joyce, Vladimir Nabokov, and many more.

In his translation into English of *A Hero of Our Time*, Nabokov alerts us to Lermontov's narrators: there the five ostensibly separate stories add up into a novel, "interlacings," as Nabokov calls them, that "grow, revolve, reveal, and mask their contours, turn away and reappear in a new attitude or light like five mountain peaks attending a traveler along the meanders of a Caucasian canyon road. The traveler is Lermontov, not Pechorin," says Nabokov, suggesting here a fudging between author and his central character over which one we need not fret.[8] Lermontov, pioneer that he was, took his stumblings for assets. Nabokov, for his part, does not fault him too much either, being free to read him as generously as possible.

Anton Chekhov's "Gooseberries" uses what apparently is a frame, but which needs to be studied better than a mere storyteller's device deserves, if Sean O'Faolain's claim that it is one of "the best short stories ever written" is to be justified.[9] In Conrad, Marlow has been cavalierly overlooked, and when remembered is made to serve for Conrad's persona, which is that much disservice to the novelist's art. For behind the narrator stands the persona, as indeed it is behind the latter that we find the author.

In Joyce's "Araby" we have to consider the narrator as quite a memoirist in order to account for the highly charged language of the text. Frank O'Connor is more shrewd, if indeed this is shrewdness pursued on purpose: he reserves the larger meaning of his stories, so to speak, for the more daring, if apparently humble, collaborator. It is only when you pry the narrator loose from the "moment" of the narrative, say, in "The Man of the World" and in "My Oedipus Complex," that you gain access to the rich core, not merely the pulp, of the fruit. In comparison, "Guests of the Nation" is too straightforward, and thus too much of an episode in history and less a self-contained, autonomous work of fiction.

In Arguilla, as we may recall, the reader allows himself only a love story unless he perseveres beyond the home-coming. With a first-person narrator, reading can become a different level of experience indeed, much in the same way that plans for a Sunday excursion eventuate into a joyful discovery of a countryside. A culture-based collaboration with the text pulls the narrator away from some stereotypical tasks assigned to him by convention.

Formal storytelling evolved out of these conventions. Annals precede formal narratives as we know them today. Royal authority needed objective lists of events in the social order, disruptions in the reign. In reaction to the starkness of this, the "cronica" evolved employing a scribe particularly minded to record what would gratify his patron. The form seemed appropriate to the age of exploration and discovery.

Although the literatures of Asia emerged from orality and its traditions, the power-that-be of colonized Asia and Southeast and Southasia found the chronicle quite suited to their needs, authority being still its source as well as audience. Then the discovery of printing liberated the scribe. Only after narration was freed thus from direct authority did the historian's career begin.

What we must remember, then, is that the singular voice of the narrator grew out of a long process, authority assuming omniscience and control at the start. It is this voice that has been with us in nearly all these years under colonialism. Sacramentalized into myth, stories depended all the more on the leverage of "Once upon a time...."

Every culture, nonetheless, has its own favored story-telling form. The popularity in Japan of the "I" narrator is perhaps a break from the culture's huge store of folklore and history. Modern Indonesian and Thai writing began, we are told, with epistolary reports, accounts of visits or sojourns in the West. There is a claim that the Tagalog novel grew out of trips to the city by locals who, on rejoining cohorts at the corner *sari-sari* store, felt obliged to regale the stay-at-homes with accounts of their adventures. If true, a thing to wonder about is why the first person is not found more frequently in Filipino letters.

It is here that the convention of being told stories from above, as it were, may be traced. For in Philippine society, listening to voices of authority has become something of a convention. Listening and hearing, that is, and not necessarily acting on the words or message heard. Thus, we have listeners and viewers, and not that many readers, in comparison. Hence, in any case, the paucity of books about ourselves and our experiences as a people—the Japanese Occupation and World War II, Bataan and EDSA, for example

—that is to say, books informed by singular viewpoints, animated by the first-person speaking voice. Perhaps this is that explanation, or part thereof. And from this derives, it seems to me, a lack of alertness to the first-person narrator in the fictions that we read.

It is in the first-person narrative that we form the habit of listening to some other and, eventually, to ourselves, and thus put the world in some kind of order. We have to snap out of having to be always told, however distant the voice. We seem ill-prepared to hear the singular and private voice owing to having been habituated to anticipating voices from elsewhere.

Fiction affords us the opportunity to acquire and develop a new skill, a new way—in our culture, that is—of discovering the world. Fiction provides us with exercises to enable us to read public as well as private experiences more meaningfully rendered. The narrative is "a means by which human beings represent and structure the world."

The narrator is our guide to that ever new order. He takes us to the territory that lies beyond Porto-Vecchio, where some other reality invites comparison with our own.

Notes

1. Abraham H. Lass and Leonard Kriegel, *Masters of the Short Story* (New York: New American Library, 1971), p. 53.
2. Rene Wellek, "Realism in Literature," in *Dictionary of the History of Ideas* (New York: Charles Scribner's Sons, 1973), IV, pp. 51-52.
3. *Ibid.*
4. *Ibid.*
5. Sartre, *op. cit.*, p. 172.
6. Sartre, *op. cit.*, p. 29.
7. Sartre, *op. cit.*, p. 39.
8. Vladimir Nabokov, "Translator's Foreword" in *A Hero of Our Time.* Translated in collaboration with Dmitri Nabokov (New York: Doubleday Anchor Books, 1958), pp. vi-vii.
9. Lewis Nicholas, "Talk with Mr. O'Faolain," in *Storytellers and Their Art.* Georgianne Trask and Charles Burkhart, ed. (New York: Anchor Books, 1963), p. 225.

3. The Lady with the Dog and Other Infatuations

*In which we deal with Anton Chekhov's legacy to litera-
ture and, in particular, to the Third World Sensibility.
We endure the defeats that his characters survive by
continually aspiring for honesty in their lives.*

To William Butler Yeats (1865-1939), his countryman Frank
O'Connor (1903-1965) has done for Ireland what Anton
Chekhov has for Russia. But it should not surprise anyone if
a reader in the late 1980s would ask: Who is Anton
Chekhov? How is he related to one of the officers of the
spaceship "Enterprise"?

For there are more movie fans than readers these days;
but while, to the former, the *New Yorker* could be a familiar
enough name, that that magazine owed its earliest success to
the short story as invented by Chekhov would be a statement
not worth a thought. Nor would the claim that "Gooseberries," as Sean O'Faolain once said, is "the best short story
ever written."[1] Once proscribed in his native land, Chekhov is
about as close as anyone can get to being an international
literary treasure, but that would be a fact of no particular
interest.

An ecstatic Katherine Anne Porter was once commis-
sioned to make a scenario of one of Chekhov's masterpieces,
the story "La Cigale." The task was demanding, and she gave
it her all. But Hollywood had its own scale of values; her
diligence, it turned out, was simply out of place. Crushed, she
literally took her money and ran. Generation after·generation
of short story writers have since taken Chekhov's work on
faith, treating it not as material suitable for transformation into
forms other than those the author had intended; critics

belabored their not finding novels by him. They had to be happy with what there is, realizing that to study the short story in the West is, to all intents and purposes, to study Anton Chekhov.

An earlier Katherine was among Anton Chekhov's students—Katherine Mansfield, a banker's daughter. From her native New Zealand she went to London at fifteen. Besides being appropriately impressed by tall city buildings there, she also found a literary community hospitable to her then-underdeveloped provincial talents. The Chekhov texts in the Constance Garnett translations could not have come at a more opportune time. In due course, she discovered "The Black Monk," "The Darling," and "Sleepyhead." Small wonder, Katherine Mansfield's indebtedness to the Russian is well documented, all the seemingly too personal details pre-served.[2] Like her literary idol, Katherine Mansfield had been afflicted with tuberculosis. When Chekhov died, she was sixteen but already making a name for herself. How good it would be, she is known to have said, if, besides stories and plays, he had an heir. A son, perhaps, whom she might be allowed to look after....

Outside of the fact that admirers of Chekhov make up a distinguished roster that includes Maxim Gorky, Isaac Babel, James Joyce and many others, the folklore of the classroom continually reminds student and teacher both that Chekhov "is greater than de Maupassant" and that there has hardly been any writer of short stories who "has failed to be in-fluenced by what he did."[3]

He is not the easiest writer to write about, however. All the things that have been said about him over the years only seem to mythify his stature while at the same time making him more personable and closer to us. George Woodcock has described perhaps for the quintessential Chekhov reader our complex but not puzzling experience with the stories:

> There are (in Chekhov) no philosophies being
> worked out, though there is an intense moral

awareness; there are no political themes, though there is an active compassion; there is no forest of symbols awaiting us, though we move through a landscape rich with images and we encounter a company of characters who live in our minds as authentic human beings because of the vivid particularity with which they and their setting are presented. This, the presentation of characters and situations that existed in concrete vitality, is realism at its highest. Such realism seems to make explanation unnecessary and hence interpretation is difficult for the conventional academic critic, even though Chekhov's work may be extraordinary accessible to the reader...who is content to take him with open eye and ear and mind.[4]

Our present discussion would indeed be a superfluity were it not for our being Filipinos. For to read him in translation is handicap enough, despite the promises of illumination described above. Actually, besides comprehending the text, the task of "listening" to Chekhov's language only begins. Why so? How different are we Filipinos from the typical Western reader of the Chekhov story? Do we really hear him? Is the fact that he was a slave's son of any special meaning to us?

Our peculiar circumstances, as readers of the Chekhov story, are perhaps not unrelated to our colonial history. Which hints, perhaps, at why W. Somerset Maugham, who comes from the metropolis, disdains him. Allow me to relate a Manila episode by way of illustration.

On one occasion I was invited to speak before a Manila women's group, and for my subject I offered "Women in My Life," hardly meaning of course a public confession but rather merely a faithful description of the women characters in the books and stories that I have read in the course of a 25-year teaching career. I must have succeeded in conveying to my audience a sense of the fictive creations I had chosen. I practically went big on Chekhov's Olga Ivanovna, in the story entitled "The Darling." Tolstoy is said to have cried upon reading it.

In the language of certain of our high school ma'ams, Olga is a woman who can't help having a man. She isn't of course that at all. Many a virtuous character meets early death thus in some of our classrooms! In any event, I must have succeeded in correcting the impression; but who could say it was not the first time that my audience had heard about Olga Ivanovna? Then before the customary question-and-answer period, a very handsome matron stood up at the far end of the room and, with all the pride and joy that her five-foot-two and 40-year-old figure could muster, her rosiest of cheeks and most impressively marcelled hair notwithstanding, she announced to us all: "My name is Olga also!"

It is not often that we identify ourselves this openly with the world of Chekhov's making; and when we do, we are happily, if not in fact pridefully, surprised. There must be a feeling, now nearly a century old, that a good many people belong to the special world Chekhov created. We belong to his slew of decent people, rich and poor alike; to his redoubtable and hypocritical folk, now claiming membership in one class, now in some other; to his deprived children and their oppressed and often oppressive parents; to his wanderers and searchers. And we observe that Chekhov does not judge them; he is almost invariably loath to speak ill of them. Rather, he merely portrays them for what they are. "Few writers have been less given to judging the lives of their creations," says one anthologist.[5] To which we might add: few readers have been unmoved by the stories and ungrateful, for they have been shown life in all its beauty and pain. Best of all, they have been shown life but, tactfully, were spared the suffering.

But Chekhov does judge, we must hasten to say. Read rightly, the stories tell you where their creator stands. Once recognized for what they are and their counterparts identified in so-called real life, Chekhov's characters can be responsible, even abominable. He hides his dislikes, of course; with a slight shift in focus, he is able to underplay the event and make his reader less critical—even overly annoyed, for that matter, as in the case of Byelokurov, in "The House with the Mansard," whose kith and kin are to be found all over the Third World plantation society.

Not too long ago, the papers carried the story of barrio shopkeepers whose business got vastly improved when to their little coastal town arrived, one day, a couple of hundred strangers, survivors of an overloaded ferry from Manila that had been lost in a storm. While awaiting the arrival of rescue parties that would return them to Manila or send them to their original destination, they unwittingly contributed to the town's commerce and its grasping and calculating store-keepers. The newspaper story had singled out one of the most successful of these entrepreneurs. The stranded pas-sengers could not have been as free-spending as the town merchants might have wished, but the merchants preyed on them nonetheless. Their plight brought to mind Chekhov's "In the Ravine," which, as you may well remember, described how a village shopkeeper, like his barrio counterparts, expe-rienced an increase in sales at his shop when one of his sons, a cop from the city, came home for his brother's wedding. To enhance the festive air, he handed out money right and left.

The father did not know at first that the banknotes were counterfeit. When he did, he had an awful time trying to distinguish the genuine from the fake paper money in the pile that he thought new business had brought in on the occasion of his son's wedding.

The story is not about him, though; and this is one of life's saving graces. In taking advantage of the role his minor characters project, Chekhov is able to provide ironies more poignant than intended, giving a new depth to the situation where the story began. In the case of our village storekeeper, for example, it is as if life offered up to the consummate artist the sinking of an overloaded interisland ferry for the sole purpose of underscoring greed, one abomination among many that people who have become all too recent victims of misfortune have still to face.

In "The Kiss" is the hapless Riabovich who, in one of those obligatory parties that we all run into in the provinces, meets an unusually revealing adventure on the nature of truth. Although otherwise a shy and dull person, he is bestowed a kiss by a lady he meets in one of the back rooms in the home of his host. Suddenly excited over the possibilities of a romance, he is transformed into an archetypal seeker, truth being in this instance the mysterious source of that peppermint-scented kiss. For weeks, and even months on end, the identity of the lady eludes him; we leave him restored to his dull old self, a contented reader of a newspaper of his day not inappropriately called *Messenger of Europe*.

Self-knowledge at first escapes Kovrin, the central character in "The Black-Monk," another of Chekhov's archetypal seekers. But after being thrown off-track by his illusions of genius, he finds his way into acquiring at least a sense of "the vanity of the world."

> He thought of the great price which life demands for the most trivial and ordinary benefit which is given men. To reach a chair of philosophy under forty years of age; to be an ordinary professor; to expound commonplace thoughts—and these thoughts of others—in feeble, tiresome, heavy language; in one word, to attain the position of a learned mediocrity, he had studied fifteen years, worked day and night, passed through a severe psychical disease, survived an unsuccessful marriage—been guilty of many follies and injustices which was torture to remember. Kovrin now clearly realized that he was a mediocrity, and he was willingly reconciled to it, for he knew that every man must be satisfied with what he is.

Kovrin's soul brothers are all over the Chekhovian countryside. After Riabovich, there is Likharyoff of "On the Way," with a Mlle. Illoviasky for travelling companion to "the ends of the earth"—if only she might forgive him "his age, his failures, his misfortunes" and go with him neither questioning nor reasoning. But would she? They resume of course their respective journeys, and the most the venturesome Likharyoff can say is: "Well, God bless you. Don't think ill of me." Chekhov the idealist makes a monument of him, nevertheless:

> For a long time he stood as if rooted to the spot, and gazed at the track left by the sledge-runners. The snowflakes settled swiftly on his hair, his beard, his shoulders. But soon the traces of the sledge-runners vanished, and he, covered with snow, began to resemble a white boulder, his eyes all the time continuing to search for something through the clouds of snow.

In Chekhov's portrait of Likharyoff is considerable power, as a personal experience demonstrated to me. In the late fall of 1969, while en route to New York, I stopped overnight in Denver, Colorado, where my publisher Alan Swallow lived. He had just issued my book, *Seven Hills Away*, and had arranged to have me discuss Chekhov's stories with some graduate students at the University of Denver. How was I to know that 20 years later, in Santa Barbara, one of them would remember that evening quite well? "Do you recall which story we discussed?" I asked, for I had forgotten the occasion almost completely. "You spoke about a character of Chekhov's who stood in the snow," came the reply. "An odd fellow. He claimed he had great capacity for belief—that was his distinction."

It was heartening to know that he remembered Likharyoff so well, this character who could claim, without as much as a shred of self-consciousness: "In my soul Nature planted an exceptional capacity for belief." His gamut of occupations—they were, in fact, infatuations!—included Science, Archeology, Popular Culture and, last but not least, Women. We should point out that he anticipated Women's Studies by a good hundred years. In any event, Mlle. Illoviasky personified his new belief.

For the first time in her life she saw before her a man in the ecstasy of a burning, prophetic faith. Gesticulating—rolling his eyes, he seemed insane and ecstatical; but in the fire of his eyes, in the torment in his words, in all the movements of his gigantic body, she saw only such beauty, that, herself not knowing what she said, she stood silently before him as if rooted to the ground, and looked into his eyes.

A unique personality, even in Chekhov. Small wonder that my Santa Barbara friend couldn't forget him if he made the effort. For, once in Chekhov's world, quitting it is not exactly easy. His characters leave a mark in our imagination that is indelible. Dmitri and Anna in "The Lady with the Dog" are two such "immortals." For all their failure as lovers, or perhaps because of it, they are simply unforgettable. You make no effort to even remember their names, and Yalta haunts you as very few places in the world do. For in Chekhov, character and setting achieve a symbiotic relationship, as of course they should. What is remarkable yet is that Chekhov does not hide his responsibility for creating this spell.

When they got out of the droshky at Oreanda they sat down on a bench not far from the sea, without talking. Yalta could be dimly discerned through the morning mist, and white clouds rested motionless on the summits of the mountains. Not a leaf stirred. The grasshoppers chirruped, and the monotonous hollow roar of the sea came up to them, speaking of peace, of the eternal sleep lying in wait for us all. The sea had roared like this long before there was any Yalta or Oreanda, it was roaring now, and it would go on roaring just as indifferently and hollowly, when we had passed away, and it will be that in this continuity, this utter indifference to life and death lies the secret of our ultimate salvation, of the stream of life on our planet, and of its never-ceasing movement towards perfection.

It is on our own level that Chekhov would like to have us experience the poignancy of belated love accommodating itself to the conventions of morality. This tact is characteristic of Chekhov. Adultery is not the story's concern but rather the evolution of passion into honesty, the emergence of the ideal beyond the tawdry. The contrast created the banality of banality; the flight towards truth seems unresolved. But this condition is precisely what the story is about: it is an ending that is the dread of the tyrants of plot, but it is nothing if not the most honest possible celebration of truth.

> "Stop crying, my dearest," he (Gurov) said. "You've had your cry, now stop... Now let us talk, let us try and think what we are to do."
> Then they discussed their situation for a long time, trying to think how they could get rid of the necessity of hiding, deception, living in different towns, being so long without meeting. How were they to shake off these intolerable fetters?
> "How? How?" he repeated, clutching his head. "How?" And it seemed to them that they were within an inch of arriving at a decision, and that then a new, beautiful life would begin. And they both realized that the end was still far, far away, and that the hardest, the most complicated part was only just beginning.

Do we have cynicism here? In the indifference, say, that Nature has reserved for our lovers? But we are no stranger to this indifference either. We've encountered it in Russian literature ever since Turgenev: Chekhov has always been our contemporary.

In his essay, "The Slave's Son," Frank O'Connor observes that there is no satisfactory critical work on Chekhov and "that is scarcely to be wondered at. He has been a victim of more enthusiastic misunderstanding than any short-story writer, praised for the wrong reasons and imitated in ways that would have astonished him. In literature as in life, he was a difficult man, diffident and evasive, hard to pin down..."[6] Frank O'Connor wrote this some years back; he may well have described the situation today. For, although Chekhov is continually read and re-read, every reader and admirer discovers a different writer. Take Thomas Mann's Chekhov, for example. How different his Chekhov is from W. Somerset Maugham's.

One problem is not in Chekhov's alleged difficulty but in what Thomas Mann identified as "modesty." This was initially mistaken for restraint, even perhaps a failure in "energeia," or Aristotle's "actualization of the potential that exists in character and situation."[7] Worse is that it serves as the tacit invitation to open-endedness and seeming incompleteness. What Chekhov actually does often is to leave the action in his narrative seemingly in the air, indeterminate, so as to underscore the pattern of meaning he has created and completed. In that pattern, plot is a secondary element.

W. Somerset Maugham spoke of "writing in the Chekhov manner" as an effort of dubious virtue altogether. He wrote in *Summing Up*:

> I do not know if I could ever have written stories in the Chekhov manner. I did not want to. I wanted to write stories that proceeded, tightly knit, in an unbroken line from the exposition to the conclusion. I saw the story as a narrative of a single event, material or spiritual, to which by the elimination of everything that was not essential to its elucidation a dramatic unity could be given.... In short I wanted to end my stories with a full-stop rather than with a straggle of dots.[8]

And this view has had a long-lasting effect among, I'd say, Malaysian, Indonesian, and Anglo-Indian story writers, many of whom held up "Rain" to iconic prominence. Some years back I had the good fortune to read for a Hong Kong-based magazine supplement featuring short fiction; from what came in the mail, it was apparent that the writers of the Region could not quite shed off the Maugham influence. I hope the situation no longer obtains; nonetheless, I've tried to escape literary jury duty to minimize meeting with Maugham's ghosts.

Chekhov's customary brevity, in any case, has been a godsend to editors, these gentlemen being always in need of space; but to writers the "slice of life" narrative is the bonus. It attained quite an ascendancy in the thirties and forties. One of the most abominable phrases in the literature of fiction came just about then. I am referring to "short shorts" and its companion term, "vignettes." Nobody seems to refer to Chekhov's short novel as "novelettes," which one might just as well do and get away with.

But somehow readers have always preferred "stories" even when long pieces like "The Black Monk," "The Steppe," "La Cigale" and others are referred to. The Russians seem satisfied with the terms "novel" and "story," calling a work one or the other, as the case may be. My point here is that Chekhov has in fact thrived within the simplest of taxonomies, "unsurpassed in European literature" as his art is, in the words of Thomas Mann.

There is some lesson to be learned here. Mann thought that Chekhov's "modesty," although an "endearing virtue, was not conducive to making the world consider him great and important; indeed it could be said that by this modesty he set the world a bad example." Chekhov rose to the "mastery of his form" as he grew in "sensitivity toward the social evils of his time—in other words, his deepening awareness of what is condemned by society, and the dying, as well as that which is to come; in short, the connection between the aesthetic and the ethical. It is surely this connection, which gives to the industriousness of art its dignity, its meaning, its usefulness," Mann went to say. It also explains he believed, Chekhov's "immense respect for work itself, his disapproval of all idle parasitism, his increasingly outspoken condemnation of a life which, as he said, 'is based on slavery'."[9]

One gets a feeling somehow that while Thomas Mann

made this observation more than thirty years ago, his words have a special relevance in the Third World. Especially telling is Chekhov's position on parasitism, so subduedly presented in "The House with the Mansard," the landowner there being its exemplar and the narrator a follower, although probably a redeemable one. It is suggested here that dormant creativity serves no purpose, and that the aspiration to change and reform is non-negotiable once we realize that offering the best in ourselves is but the beginning. An infinite number of insoluble problems of life awaits us. Take a nihilistic or existential view, if you like; but these problems will remain nonetheless. Try a phenomenological and symbolic tactic as well; and, as in Gurov's case in "The Lady with the Dog," promise of relief will be right ahead, except that yet other problems will emerge. You have just begun, as indeed the Gurovs of the world have discovered.

It is for this reason perhaps that Thomas Mann called "vague" Chekhov's vision of "human perfection." But he is pleased that Chekhov would not have us forget that "working —giving form to truth, hoping darkly, sometimes almost confidently, truth and serene form will avail to set free the human spirit and prepare mankind for a better, a lovelier, worthier life."

Earlier on, his own disciple, Maxim Gorky, once said that he had "never known anyone feel so deeply that work is the basis of all culture as Chekhov did." There is in fact a famous letter of Chekhov which situates the contemporary Third World intellectual in the brotherhood. There Chekhov gives a thorough account of his beginnings as the "son of a serf":

> a one-time shop assistant, a choir boy, schoolboy and university student, brought up to fawn on rank, kiss the hands of priests, accept without questioning other people's ideas, express his gratitude for every morsel of bread he eats, a young man who has been fre-quently whipped, who goes to give lessons without galoshes, engages in street fights, tortures animals, loves to go to his rich relatives for dinner, behaves

hypocritically toward God and man without the slightest excuse but only because he is conscious of his own worthlessness...

And this young man goes to Moscow—very much in the manner a young Malay would go to Kuala Lumpur, or a Cebuano would proceed to Manila for college work. In the city he manages to support himself by writing sketches for the magazines and later enters medical school. Somehow he makes a writer out of himself. Could you write a story about this young man? Chekhov asked his friend Souvorin. About "how this young man squeezes the slave out of himself drop by drop?"

The situation is hauntingly familiar, the tension between metropolis and country sharing a commonality with Third World experience. We in the Philippines, in short, could have learned from Chekhov years ago.

But that did not happen. For three or four generations we sought and took for models the works of those whom Chekhov had earlier influenced—the Katherine Mansfields, the James Joyces, the Katherine Anne Porters, etc., etc.[10] There was, moreover, a whole slew of information about literature to learn. Besides the literature and its conventions, there was the culture which all that embodied. The learning process could hardly be called slight; we had to do everything in a received language, every single word truly an alien presence. A sensibility had to be evolved and cultivated, and the self taught to respond willy-nilly to the received culture and its implications in terms of political and economic forces. These accommodations drain the nation of its energies.

There is a saying that the Devil has a trick to deceive good people; he entices them to do more than they are able so that they are not able to do anything else.[11] Could this be the reason why, individually and collectively, our energies got spent and, in our stupor, we had to let things ride?.

In story after story by Chekhov, we see his characters trying ever so hard to cope, to attain dignity and cherish their vision of the better life, although only to be denied success, to be betrayed and defeated. Still, thanks to his narrative art, we merely observe the failure, betrayal and defeat, unlike his characters who seemed fated to endure them and do. We suffer for them, but with a sense of tentativeness born out of the certainty that they themselves will find relief, being now armed with self-knowledge and a determination to gather the shards of their lives together.

Do we have that self-knowledge ourselves? No matter, since to the Chekhov character—and perhaps to us, also—it's this being engaged and working towards the better life that counts. We meet this spirit page after page. In the innocent Vanka as well as in the obsessed Kovrin, we are simultaneously Vanka and not Vanka; we are Kovrin and yet not Kovrin. Chekhov makes us realize this, and this is the enduring Chekhov. His art asks us to remember who we are and what we might become. To paraphrase his own words, he enables us to shed every drop of the colonial in us and become free, just as the slave's son squeezed every drop of the slave in him and left the world a rich legacy.

Notes

1. Trask and Burkhart, *op. cit.*, p. 225.
2. James H. Pickering, *Fictions 100* (New York: Macmillan, 1985, p. 1158.)
3. Lass and Kriegel, *op. cit.*, p. 208.
4. George Woodcock, "Master of Modesty and Others," *Sewanee Review*, XCVII:2 (Spring 1989), p. 309.
5. Lass and Kriegel, *op. cit.*, p. 208.
6. Frank O'Connor, *The Lonely Voice* (New York: Harper Colophon Books, 1985), p. 101.
7. John Gardner, *The Art of Fiction* (New York: Vintage, 1985), p. 1185.
8. Trask and Burkhart, *op. cit.*, pp. 40-41.
9. *Ibid.*, p. 329.
10. In *James Joyce* by Chester G. Anderson (London: Thames and Hudson, Ltd., 1967) is this interesting note (p. 52): "If these stories

("Eveline"and "After the Race" by James Joyce) with the combination of realism and symbolism in an open-ended form seem less original now than they did then, it is only because Joyce and Chekhov arrived almost simultaneously at similar techniques which gave the modern short story its main line of development."

11. Actually this is a paraphrase from St. Vincent de Paul, quoted in "Reflection" for November 13, 1988, in Anon., *Every Day Is a Gift.* Introduction by Rev. Fredrick Schroeder (New York: Catholic Book Publishing Co., 1984), p. 165.

4. The Novel and Its Reader

An overview of what is involved when we read a novel, and what creativity at this level means; how to deal with our alleged cultural deprivations, the difference between fiction and history, and the roles that film and TV play in disabling the imagination and sensibility.

The shopping area in Cubao is not exactly the center of metropolitan Manila; but on any Saturday afternoon you'll probably see milling about there five people to, on the average, every ten square meters of sidewalk or street. It's a fascinating scene to watch. Especially from the vantage point of some coffee shop, what with its glass-walled front lending a sense of energy and urgency to the scene, you get a feeling that that crowd out there is capable of just about anything.

"How would it be," I once asked a companion, also a fellow writer, "if all of these people were readers—our readers?" And even before my companion could offer an answer, I added: "Can you possibly imagine any one of them, singled out of every ten, sitting in a corner, somewhere, absorbed in a novel?"

My companion laughed. "Or any book for that matter!" Which was wishful thinking on my part; but, recalling the incident now, I couldn't help wondering how we, as a people regard reading. A report in the paper the other day said that of 33,681,424 Filipinos aged from 10 to 75, some 5,820,233 are illiterate. To the Department of Education, Culture, and Sports, "illiteracy" means "the failure or inability of a person to read and write a simple message in any dialect."[1] Which is like saying let's forget books and literature altogether. And this, again, is neither here nor there.

The numbers, though, are disturbing. If you are generous enough, you'd say we have no monopoly of problems. I recall Robert Scholes saying that stories are today the opiate that has replaced what Marx once singled out.[2] Indeed, it requires no leap of the imagination to realize that we live in a world of stories, real as well as imagined; and that we respond to them often with consuming attention. There is a stupor in the eyes of those teen-agers, young adults and middle-aged who, being spared a more fatal vice, allow themselves to be merely addicted to comic books; and matching the miasma of "Tarzan" or "Twilight Zone" are bits of pap offered by the daily press. Besides the manner of their presentation to the so-called reading public, there is in current events a surreal quality that one wishes to sleep away but simply cannot. To read these days, a thinking person risks being stunned or maimed. Illiteracy does offer some advantage.

But what happens when, in all seriousness of purpose, we read? And novels, in particular, should not be extraneous in the context we treat reading here. For, if indeed, novels are stories, and stories have become today's opium, we should know how to deal with them.

Of the numerous art forms that the Filipino has worked with, storytelling seems to be the one he has held considerable hope for, in relation to his society's articulation with history. I trust that I shall be able to convey a sense of this theme.

There is one particular consideration to take into account: those figures from the Department of Education, Culture and Sports notwithstanding, the art and craft of the storyteller is central to our nationhood. Rare is the nation with a novelist for national hero. Thus, to know what novels are, what their writing entails and what their writers ask of us as readers, is for the individual as well perhaps as for the nation, a decisive step toward self-knowledge.

Our folk epics, along with the *awit* and *corrido* of a later period, set us on track. Followed the town plaza *entablado*, then the legitimate theater, lending us a new approach, a more direct one, towards the telling of our story. Printing and the vitality of the vernaculars led to popular entertainments which, if blatantly romantic, held their ground in the twenties and to this day. Future study will reveal how, structurally speaking, with romantic love for its disguise in our popular fiction and theater, the same passion that inspired writers from Balagtas to the present burns undiminished today in the heart of the Filipino. There is a secret here: in his own idiosyncratic way, the Filipino cherishes a culture and a geography.

To discover this secret, however, we need to understand a process widely used but not readily objectified and certainly rarely described. It deals with literary effects and responses we experience but which are largely unidentified. We simply have not become aware of the phenomenon which makes reading a novel not unlike visiting a place and living there for a length of time and then cherishing the experience in our memory.

In Sartre's definition of that relationship—"To write," he says, "is to disclose the world and offer it as a task to the generosity of the reader..."—is our access to that secret. He calls the novel an "exigence" and a "gift." What kind of attention, then, may the reader provide to cope with that urgency, and what thanks can he offer in return for the gift?

Rather than face this issue, Sartre would have us know that "given this world with its injustices, it is not so that I might contemplate them coldly, but that I might animate then with my indignation, that I might disclose them and create them with their nature as injustices, that is, as abuses to be suppressed."[3] To Sartre, then, exigence means commitment.

Hugely desirable as that may be, phenomenological considerations would have us observe the space between reading and action. The process is well worth describing, and for this our thanks must go to Wolfgang Iser, who, in *The Implied Reader* presents the nap and pile of the reading experience. With concepts drawn from Roman Ingarden, Edmund Husserl,

M. Merleau-Ponty, Gilbert Ryle, B. Ritchie, and others, Iser leaves practically no stone unturned to reveal an approach to a text. He offers a veritable course on how to read, and for reward we discover how literature allows us the "chance to formulate the unformulated."[4]

As with Sartre, Iser would have the reader complete the novel. To begin with, such a text has two poles, the artistic and the esthetic. The first is the text created by the writer, and for this he has an implied reader in mind; the second is the text created by the reader, a realization on the latter's part: in so doing he becomes its actual reader. What is written and what is realized do not necessarily match; indeed gaps are to be expected when, imaginatively, the second is laid upon the first.

These gaps are, in fact, important and necessary: they mobilize the imagination. To engage the reader, the literary work must provide him the pleasure of active play, whose parameters are boredom and overstrain. Thus the reader's imagination animates the written text, giving the latter a greater significance that they could likely have effected on their own. What the text provides and what the reader brings to it in this manner converge into a virtual world, as dis- tinguished from the actual world it may have been derived from.[5]

The novel we read is created in terms of what Roman Ingarden calls "intentional sentence correlatives." These are data available at the sentence level, for Ingarden believes that in literary works sentences are not merely statements. It is absurd to have them perform only at that level of usefulness. In truth, writers assign them other tasks besides merely providing information. What gives a text literary quality is its ability to go beyond merely saying what it seems to say. Such sentences are thus the field for the interaction of correlatives, the sum of which becomes the "world presented" by the work. It is these intentional sentence correlatives impinging on each other all through the text that generate reader response, creating what Ingarten calls "sequent intentional sentence correlatives."[6]

Being shaped all the while in the reader's mind are expectations generated by those correlatives, and the process goes on even as the sentences provide, each one of them, more expectations of what is to come. Edmund Husserl calls these expectations "pre-intentions."[7] The act of reading becomes a continuity of modifications—i.e., of pre-intentions modified and remodified. Each modification creates a horizon relative to what is expected. When that point is reached, a retrospection occurs: thus, a continuity of anticipation and retrospection. We might visualize this as horizons reached and then receding only to be replaced by yet other horizons, even as the text reveals, on and on, Iser would say, "its potential multiplicity of connections."

> This is why the reader often feels involved in events which, at the time of reading, seem real to him, even though in fact they are very far from his own reality. The fact that completely different readers can be differently affected by the "reality" of a particular text is ample evidence of the degree to which literary texts transform reading into a creative process that is far from mere perception of what is written. The literary text activates our faculties, enabling us to recreate the world it presents.[8]

In an early essay on how a novel is made out of the density of detail that its writer can offer, Ortega y Gasset writes: "The novel must be caught in a dense web of innumerable minutely told circumstances. What is our life but an immense agglomeration of trifles?" He cites Marcel Proust as a master of density; and great novels are, says Ortega y Gasset, "essentially lavish of particulars. Indeed, the books of Cervantes, Stendhal, Dickens, Dostoevsky are of the tightly packed sort... Great novels are atolls built by myriads of tiny animals whose seeming frailness checks the impact of the seas."[9]

Virtuality is what comes from this density. The effect does not derive from the text itself, says Iser; nor from the reader's imagination, either. When the text and the reader's imagination work together, a new dimension emerges from the experience of reading, and this is the dimension of virtuality.[10]

The reader creates a gestalt out of the material on the page, subjecting the given to realizations that cannot, however, exceed what has been provided. The reason for this is that the reader cannot possibly exhaust the text at all, since it is certain that every sentence could go beyond itself, so that the whole work becomes a continuum of anticipation and retrospection. Indeed, no story can be completely told.

But it thrives and lives in the imagination, owing to a quality Iser calls "indeterminacy."[11] Omissions, paradoxically enough, make the story dynamic. Each reading offers us the "horizons" that Ortega y Gasset spoke of, "the circle of people and events that integrate the world of each of us." In the novel, our perception of this world varies with each reading.[12] "With all literary texts," says Iser, "a second reading...often produces a different impression from the first. The reason may lie in the reader's own change of circumstances; still, the text must be such as to allow this variation. On a second reading familiar occurrences now tend to appear in a new light and seem to be at times corrected, at times enriched."

Iser gives a further illustration of the reason for the variation in the impressions that readers obtain. Given the limitations of written as opposed to the unwritten text, the experience may be likened to "two people gazing at the night sky...both may be looking at the same collection of stars, but one will see the image of a plough and the other will make out a dipper. The 'stars' in the literary text are fixed; the lines that join them are variable." But no author will provide his readers with a predetermined configuration for those stars, drawing those lines himself. To do so is to drive his reader away; hence, indeterminacy, which allows the reader to make his own picture consistent with the gestalt.[13]

Then how is consistency achieved? Through a process

familiar to our comprehension of the images, for "it is the guess of the beholder that tests the medley of forms and colours for coherent meaning, crystallizing it unto shape when a consistent interpretation has been found," says E.R. Gombrich.[14] An interesting phase follows: it is at this point that illusions are created.

The images created by the text is what is meant here. These are adjusted now and again within the continuum of modifications. If reading results in a build-up of illusions, oddly enough we lose contact with reality. And Northrop Frye calls reality, in this context, the negation of illusions.[15] An excess of negation seems just as dangerous as an excess of illusion, for in the first is sheer reality; the other becomes escape.

Throughout this process of building and negating illusions, the virtuality of the world created is the reader's guide. The balance of negation and creation of illusions is afforded by the text, but is never the same at any two points in time. This condition gives the text what Iser calls "productive value."[16]

Illusion-building, however, must be understood as a transitory state. We cannot afford to be permanently caught in it, although in reading popular fiction or detective stories, where anticipations and retrospection pursue what might be called a close direction, we do get help in dispelling illusions. This comes in the form of "alien associations" which intrude but cannot be made consistent with the gestalt tentatively established. In other words, the reader has entered the unfamiliar world of the novel but occasionally slips away, allowing himself never to be caged in. This movement or "oscillation between consistency and 'alien association' is a balancing operation, ...and it is this," Iser says, "that forms the esthetic experience offered by the literary text."[17]

Thus the experience of reading indeed locates the novel's full value between what the writer has presented and what the reader is capable of bringing to it. In Iser's words, the reader gets "entangled in the 'text-gestalt' that he himself has produced.... Through this entanglement the reader is bound to open himself up to the workings of the text and so leave behind his own preoccupations...."[18] Reader-oriented criticism has also pursued a theory of "horizons" more sophisticated than that suggested by Ortega y Gasset. One proponent is Hans Robert Jauss, who would have us read a novel, for example, by being attentive to its track record in critical history. "A literary work is not an object which stands by itself and which offers the same face to each reader in each period. It is not a monument which reveals its timeless essence in a monologue."[19]

Like Iser, Stanley Fish is an advocate of the adjustments of expectations. He would work at the level of the sentence, where meaning becomes the "total movement of reading." Michael Riffaterre and Jonathan Culler, the latter particularly, stress the reader's acquisition of a "grammar of literature" such as what is available at universities.[20] "Poets and novelists write on the basis of what can be read," Culler claims. "In order to read text as literature, we must possess 'a literary competence.' "

This overview of reader-oriented criticism, particularly Wolfgang Iser's configuration of the implied reader, should have great use in our cultural life today, although I offer this possibility in trepidation. Our literary community does not seem to really impress that larger world we call nation. There is, in Philippine society and elsewhere, a distanced politeness to our assiduous literary activity. The indifference is shared elsewhere.

An international magazine, *Chelsea 46*, does not include a single Filipino poem or story, although it is an issue devoted to World Literature in English, and is one inch thick at that. I recall a *New York Times* article by a visiting American critic in which he claimed he had been impressed but amusedly puzzled over what use T.S. Eliot, Edmund Wilson, John Crowe Ransom, and the New Critics serve Filipino writers. In a *Yale Review* article reporting on a PEN conference in Manila, the writer suggested in less than guarded language that the ability of the Filipino to use English orally, let alone in writing, leaves much to be desired. Philippine PEN might have to explain, the writer said, how a certain high functionary could easily write and give away books.[21]

Which takes us away from our topic, but the point is that at best there is that distanced politeness to our literary efforts, and it is not a question of language either. Language, be it native, borrowed or received, always needs to be used well. What is important is that the world needs to be told our story, how we live and struggle on, like all others. In so doing, we at least keep in touch with ourselves and are hopefully reminded of our humanity, of our belief in a future. Optimism is the second surname of every writer, however he tries to misspell the word or avoid using it. And novels are exercises in hope and faith, however documentary and rigid they may appear to be. Over the years, it must be granted, we have achieved occasional successes; but collectively our efforts do not add up towards a strong impression. Clearly, our writers could get busier and publish more. But here we are, for now, describing what the seemingly simple act of reading entails when all along indifference is what lies ahead, our literature a bottle (with a message?) that has been tossed over the railing and left to float in a sea of illiteracy. But my feeling is we must grow wherever growth is possible; and above all we have to become, for our writers' sake, their very best readers. For good or ill, the best audience for the Filipino novels is the Filipino. It is he alone who can create our virtual world to the fullest and then understand his own. When we have readers of that caliber, who needs snobbery?

With that thought in mind, we might raise some questions. Are we sharing enough our rich store of literary competence? True, the university is an excellent place to work from; but is there a working gospel of serious interest here? How roughly, for example, we deal with genres and forms! Does *Noli Me Tangere* receive a healthy treatment as a novel in our schools? Isn't it bad enough that it has to be stuck rigidly into the school curriculum? How well do we understand the hermetically sealed text that a novel, or fiction, for that matter, must have so that it does not get mistaken for history?

In his watershed of an essay on the novel, Ortega y Gasset described the effect of the best of the genre in the following words: "The titles of certain books are like names of cities in which we used to live for a time. They at once bring back a climate, a peculiar smell of streets, a general type of people and a specific rhythm of life..."[22] How many of our school teachers offer their classes with a sense of the rhythm of life in the streets of Nick Joaquin's Manila?

What might happen if we read our novels rigorously in the many ways suggested? What would we find in the novels of the Commonwealth period? How would the novels of the Golden Period of Tagalog literature fare? Would we find in those pages a mirror of national experience per se? Or how much of our own expectations must we contribute, how much of our own anticipation and retrospection? How much more of the Martial Law years than we know will we find in the closed coffin that dominates the action and revelation in Linda Ty-Casper's *Awaiting Trespass*? We have an excellent writer in Antonio M. Enriquez; his stories set in Mindanao are the most vivid portions of literary landscape from that part of the country since A.B. Rotor wrote about Davao. But can Manila or Luzon readers bring something of themselves to those stories and discover afterwards new aspects of their own lives in them? It is this kind of adventure in sensibility that awaits the reader who knows how to read. Instead of dealing with the rigidity of predetermined structures, he might accept the invitation to excel in responding to the literary text. To seize the indeterminacy and fill the gaps in the artistic construction with materials from his own sensibility and thus attain the aesthetic fulfillment that the Filipino novel aspires to—this is the task for him.

Most readers who prefer the rigidity of history will probably be confused over the film called "A Dangerous Life." Obviously this is history and yet not quite history; and if it is the latter, then how much of a fiction is it? The viewer is obliged, as in the case of a literary text, to find the balance between consistency and alien association. Were this a written text, a measure of aesthetic enjoyment could probably be assured. This is possible by resorting to the privacy inherent in the reading experience. But viewing a film or video is a public act; one's contact with the images is drastically limited to the "flow" of the entire story. Thus illusion-building is either too distended or too abrupt, and negation becomes too intermittent or is readily distorted. The configuration towards fact or history, and illusion or reality, can be achieved under great stress and towards a too indeterminate reward. The experience, though, may be more of an entertainment than a recreation of history.

Thus, challenges to the imagination and adjustments to new precepts abound. To the Filipino novelist there is a renaissance just ahead; to his reader, a new sense of himself.

Notes

1. *Philippine Daily Globe*, Nov. 27, 1988, p. 3.
2. W.J.T. Mitchell, "Foreword," *On Narrative* (Chicago and London: University of Chicaco Press, 1881), p. viii.
3. Sartre, *op. cit.*
4. "Chance" could be the keyword here; but, in any case, Wolfgang Iser's *The Implied Reader* (Baltimor & London: John Hopkins University Press, 1974) is for now our best guide to this approach.
5. *Ibid.*, p. 277.
6. *Ibid.*
7. *Ibid., p. 278.*
8. *Ibid.*
9. Jose Ortega y Gasset, *The Dehumanization of Art and Other Writings on Art and Culture* (New York: Doubleday, 1956), pp. 89-90.
10. Iser, *op. cit.*, p. 279.
11. *Ibid.*
12. Ortega y Gasset, *op. cit.*, p. 82 .
13. Iser, *op. cit.*, p. 280.

14. E.H. Gombrich, quoted in Iser, *op. cit.*, 284.
15. Northrop Frye, quoted in Iser, *op. cit.*, p. 284.
16. Iser, *op. cit.*, p. 285.
17. *Ibid.*, p. 286.
18. *Ibid.*, p. 291.
19. Raman Selden, "Hans Robert Jauss: Horizons of Expectations," in *A Reader's Guide to Contemporary Literary Theory* (Lexington, Kentucky: The University Press of Kentucky, 1985), p. 114.
20. *Ibid.*, p. 119-22.
21. Richard Howard, "Manila Clipper," *Yale Review*, 76:2 March 1987, pp. 191-202. Howard begins as follows: "An American writer of stoical bent and belittling straightforwardness had left Manila a few days ago before I arrived, and after his visit and his pronouncements, Philippine PEN—which I was visiting on my way to the 1977 PEN Congress in Sydney—was in a dither. The writer had declared that the members couldn't manage English properly, not to say expressively, and they suspected he was right (certainly they couldn't manage English the way he did)..."
22. Ortega y Gasset, *op. cit.*, p. 81.

5. The Novel in the Third World

A note on the house of fiction and on V.S. Naipaul's A House for Mr. Biswas, Raja Rao's Kanthapura and others; and how Philippine writers might add to the list.

Over the years the idea of fiction as a house of some sort or other has become popular with serious readers. Especially with the demise of the omniscient narrator and the harried discovery of various ways of writing fiction, including those that in fact lead no further than the incorrigible storytelling self, if indeed anywhere at all, the idea of windows, fictional windows upon the world, that is, have likewise become popular. And windows assume viewers as well as scenes or landscapes to be viewed. The novelist serves his art best, if we are to believe Elizabeth Bowen, by writing without preassumptions. I take that to mean that initially he need not be too sure about what there is to see as soon as he has drawn the blinds; he need not have any definite idea about what has been arranged for him to view. Surprises are as much a part of life as they are of fiction; but their task being what it is, writers employ surprise more deliberately than life does. In life, surprises are never prearranged or contrived; they simply occur, and need not be recognized as surprises either. Indifferent nature does not care whether the word exists in our vocabulary.

As a reader—that is to say, as an occasional caller at the house of fiction—I find myself hanging around the vestibule. There I indulge my capacity for surprise while awaiting a formal welcome, such as might be accorded. I am uncomfortable with anything resembling a red carpet; but cordiality, some form of it anyhow, makes my first few minutes reassuring. The pleasures that follow, I am only too aware, must be earned.

Lately, the visit does not go this way. Early on I am made uneasy at sight of the all too familiar furniture about me. There are hired help about the place that are much too ubiquitous; my initial discomfort mounts into an anxiety. I put myself in mind of the purpose of my visit, manage the next few minutes as decorously as possible, and then take my leave.

If memory serves me right, I first met the word "furniture" used in this context in Katherine Anne Porter. She was describing, as it happened, the characters in a novel by a contemporary. By "furniture" she meant the character props that the writer finds necessary for her narrative. As a critical word, it sounds innocent enough but it seems intended to enhance our respect for the craft.[1]

Addicts of the detective story and of personal histories by world figures and proconsuls have noticed that these two kinds of reading matter, different though one may be from the other, have one feature in common. There are Filipinos in them. While reading a biography of General MacArthur I was forced to stop before the first five thousand words; for I had run into an old friend. Perforce I had to say, "Hello! How did you get here? O—*kumusta! Papaano't naririto ka!*" For my compatriot was none other than the General's driver.

How many of our countrymen have found employment as drivers, valets, and chefs in the pages of the novels and books in the West is a tempting research topic. Try, for a starter Carson McCullers's *Reflections in a Golden Eye*. And in a short story I admire very much, "The Valiant Woman" by James F. Powers, a conversation concerning the hiring of a domestic goes on as follows:

> "Fish Frawley has got himself a Filipino, John. Did you hear?"
> Father Firman leaned forward, interested. "He got rid of the woman he had?"
> "He did. It seems she snooped."

"Snooped, eh?"

"She did. And gossiped....Then he got the Filipino."[2]

I must confess to a short-lived delight on meeting these
paisanos in my reading during the late forties and early fifties.
In my critical naivete, I thought that the realism was by way
of honoring our identity as Filipinos. In John Fante, who
wrote from Hollywood, where Filipinos abound, they were
often portrayed at their sartorial best, in wing-tipped shoes
and fedoras. To one who has not shed off colonial up-
bringing, this did not seem patronizing at all. It never occurred to me then that our countrymen, real people that they
are, have been transformed into fictional furniture. In justice
to John Fante it must be said that he tried his best to make
living characters out of them. Unfortunately, he could only
create victims of class instead of personages. William Saroyan
did no better.

I was familiar at that time with the use of the word and
the fictional strategy involved; but I was diverted, I guess, by
the idea that we were being written about—however skimp-
ily, and more often patronizingly. I had the same feeling
reading about mangrove forests in Conrad and the river
scenes in "The Lagoon." And W. Somerset Maugham's des-
criptions of the low-lying, cloud-smothered coasts of the
island south of our own Mindanao told me that we can do
several of those scenes ourselves, that in fact our landscapes
are worthy of rendering also.

Imagine if Robinson Crusoe's Man Friday had been a
writer and offered us a narrative about how a Mr. Crusoe had
arrived on his island off the coast of Chile. We would have
more or less the same story we now know but one from a
different center. The viewpoint from which events are told
cannot but change them radically; in this instance, the Crusoe
story would be rendered from Friday's perspective.

Daniel Defoe's construction, a landmark in British—
meaning to say imperial—literature, would become another

story altogether. It would not be the story from which has been derived, Martin B. Green claims, the modern English novel. It is *Robinson Crusoe* (1719), he says, in *Dreams of Adventure, Deeds of Empire*, that seeded the whole crop.[3] In Alexander Selkirk, who had been marooned on one of the Juan Fernandez Islands off the coast of Chile, Defoe found to his great fortune the paradigm of the White Man's conquest and authority over the non-White world.

Green's thesis is not likely to be popular even today, but one can build a case in his favor. It is plain enough, as John Lehmann wrote in 1947, that the troops of Great Britain "have come from many of their traditional outposts and her coal no longer keeps the transport and the industry of the world running."[4] Many a great novel has resulted from the tension between the imperial and the oppressed worlds. If Crusoe has been the model for ingeniousness in adversity, his Friday has been the paradigm for servitude. This was a lesson Rudyard Kipling did not miss and, to this day, the idea is staple even in the merest spy or adventure story. Fiction has romanticized servitude even in the age of realism. Modern fiction is loath to attribute to the oppressed the sensibility it lavishes on the oppressor, and perhaps for good reason: the oppressed do not buy novels.

It was when the imperial world saw the oppressed not only as a source of service but as consumers of goods that the complex interdependence of nations became transformed into an equally complex interdependence of capital. Third World countries are those, so the definition goes, that depend for their survival and/or growth on either the First or Second World. Several years back *Time* magazine floated the concept that there is in existence a Fourth and a Fifth World, the last being what may be designated "basket cases." Political and economic considerations inspired the designation "Third World literature," which placed on shifting ground such literatures as those of Finland, Turkey, India, Sri Lanka, and several others—nations with proud literary histories but which cannot claim membership in the imperial club.

What these political and economic labels have done is deny the development of national awareness among peoples that have been unreservedly dominated by so-called First and Second World cultures, a fact abundantly rendered in the words of their writers. Where literacy has outdistanced economic growth, we may find great writing; but so may be observed the exodus of workers, as has happened in Ireland Mexico, Italy, and Greece. Sweat and brawn seem to have the habit of quitting the scene, leaving only stragglers and passable geniuses behind.

The literatures, fortunately in some cases, defy classification (except perhaps in the case of Mexico, whose writers in the class of an Octavio Paz and a Carlos Fuentes could hardly be called Third World writers) for the reason that their books may reveal a cosmopolitanism both in intention as well as in performance. These writers feel they belong to the larger world as well as their own. In short, the criterion for Third Worldism is perhaps to be arrived at from a bias other than that of politics and economics.[5]

My sense of the matter is that during the last several decades, fictional characters available for costuming or for conscription in the service of the entertainment industries have been in demand. Or, to put the matter differently, novelists have sprung from everywhere. On the other hand, Third World writers cannot bear to see their people now as furniture; least of all can this new awareness be anything but an essential concern both in their private lives as well as in fictive creations. The result is that thanks to the art and craft of the novel, it is now the once-imperial character that has become the furniture.

How different the characters are in the *Philippine Magazine* stories written by American contributors compared with those by us. Philippine writing is fortunate in that the editor, A.V.H. Hartendorp, did not see our characters as furniture—those created by, say, Manuel E. and Lydia V. Arguilla, Bienvenido N. Santos, Estrella Alfon, and, earlier, Arturo Tolentino, in their individual and collective efforts to put form to an emerging culture in a received language.Our literature would have been doomed.

We came by our illumination after World War II, the euphoria of Liberation notwithstanding. I recall Juan T. Gatbonton's "Clay" and Rony V. Diaz's "The President of the Tribe" and happily realize how the furniture has changed national origin. In my own *The Bamboo Dancers*, which was composed about the same time, Herb Lane, while not exactly a wooden pedestal for some ornamental plant, is at best a familiar sofa, soon a candidate for the scrap heap.

In this connection, it should be instructive to re-read today Javellana's *Without Seeing The Dawn* and Bienvenido N. Santos's *The Volcano* and *The Man Who (Thought He) Looked Like Robert Taylor*, as well as Celso Carunungan's *Like a Big Brave Man*. Today's issues in Philippine-American relations could derive rich insights from these works. It would be a disservice to our writers to gloss over their work under the influence of a minimalism acquired through a dependence on mere literary values. Novelists are said to be all-knowing and consummate in craftsmanship, and may be expected to breathe life into their creations. But in precisely the same way that the Western novelists go no further than make furniture out of our choice personalities—whose real-life counterparts, if any, would be real *narra* and *molave* or *kamagong*—do our novelists, we might ask, merely avail themselves of whatever stuff happens to be within reach?

This is no criticism of our writers but of our readers, even as it is merely a recognition of the separation of worlds, of distances in horizons. Beyond the reach of the naked eyes, the horizon seems to steadily descend; thus the Western view of us changes not only on account of the increased reach but also because of the elevation of the viewing tower.

Perhaps the novelists who have been most remarkable in foreshortening horizons—that is to say, in making provisions in their craft for the vicissitudes of history and the shifting of horizons—are those of Africa, India and the Caribbean. The reader of Western novels familiar with the bearers in Kipling's and porters in Hemingway's stories will find in the pages of South African and Caribbean writers evidence, among other things, of the shifted equilibrium. Thematic ideas are now fleshed out in non-White characters, nor do novels have necessarily to deal with great events. The writers prefer great themes instead. There is quite a difference, we know. Thus the spell Amos Tutuola has cast with his myths.[6]

But beyond the mythic and archetypal, which are these themes? With people who wear straw sandals, as the Chinese short-story writer Lu Xun would call us, are there great themes? Whatever the answer may be, it is from the Third World that the voices come.

Before Third World writers appeared on the world stage, Ortega y Gasset warned us that "the quarry is finite. There exists a definite number of possible themes for the novel. The workmen of the primal hour had no trouble finding new blocks—new characters, new themes. But present-day writers face the fact that only narrow and concealed veins are left them."[7] And the fledgling novelists read this with dread. "It has become practically impossible to find new subjects," the Spanish philosopher goes on further. "It is not for nothing that the novel is called 'novel.' "[8] What is worse, he adds, is that the reading public has become more fastidious even as there are fewer things for the novelist to write about.

We now know, of course, that this is a false scare. The view from the vestibule will be indeed limited, especially after our having visited with our well-situated friends several times before. But to the household staff every guest is worthy of notice, his every whimsy or frivolity the subject for, at the very least, some lively kitchen tattle. I am far from suggesting that novelists are tattletales, only that the views from the kitchen, from the yard, from the stables—these will be, and have been, different and will henceforth not pass unobserved and unrecorded. That is to say, the house of fiction does not belong exclusively to the masters anymore.

Not only has writing become democratized but it has also been indigenized. The native not only learned the language of their masters but are even using their own upon the reality that has resulted from the political and social order imposed by an earlier authority as well as by native surrogates, however the latter might wear their masks. There is today probably no prose form that is not finding support from traditions once regarded as uncouth.

At the same time, we are discovering that something is lost by staying rooted to the native tradition. From out of orality, which has had its day, the precision of the received language could be taken advantage of. R.K. Narayan's work, which is in English, provides a case in point. As Bruce King has observed, his "narrators are of a piece with the life shown in the stories, in which European and American values seem inappropriate to an eternal India. Standard British English would distance the characters and pressure the author toward explanation, thus losing the wry, understated comedy that is Narayan's hallmark. If Narayan had written in dialect, the stories would turn into farce, disturbing their careful balance of seriousness, objectivity and amusement."[9]

In the matter of using one's tradition, the Philippine experience might be cited as paradigmatic. Out of the *ladinos* of the mid-17th century emerged the command of Spanish which created Rizal's *Noli Me Tangere*. Similarly, it is India that has shown the world how, upon a verdant field of indigenous literatures, the Anglo-Indian novel has risen, begrudging as the larger world audience may be what an R.K. Narayan or a Raja Rao could make of the form. The esemplastic imagination had demonstrated many times over how it can take possession of an essentially alien form, like the novel, and press it into service for Third World culture—and liberation.

I had a most exciting experience conducting a course on Third World writers with students whose fare had been a heavy one of Western novels. After I had explained the approach I intended to take, my students worked on the assigned texts with the eagerness of thirsty boulevard promenaders at a soda fountain. I made sure not to ask for summaries of the novels, having learned what a fool requirement that is. To have a student rush through a book the writing of which must have taken months, if not years, and come anyway with a thousand-word description of what in fact the book cannot possibly be, since no book becomes itself until its reader has brought a great deal of himself to it—can anything be more preposterous? What we did was identify the strategies of narrative the author tried, establish his relationship with his material, and describe the over-all statement that the work seemed to make. What the students immediately came away with was a sense of a new world, of a community rather than a nest of individuals whose counter-interests provide the action. And best of all, the students discovered Lu Xun's straw-sandaled folk—and, of course, amid a new kind of furniture.

In Rene Maran's *Batoula*, which won the Prix Goncourt in 1922, which had gone the year before to Marcel Proust for *Remembrance of Things Past*, the class found an anti-colonial novel, though with hardly a member of the once-conquering race on the page. The colonialists have become the furniture now, which must have been what prompted Leopold Senghor to say "that the West Indian writers freed themselves from docile imitation of the Metropole and fear of their negritude."[10]

That kind of liberation is not easily achieved in literature as the shackles of enslavement and dependency are well forged. Raja Rao's opportunity to break loose came with the Gandhian movement; in his novel *Kanthapura* we have perhaps the quintessential fictional monument to that period in Indian history. Here, the violence that Western novels seek to dramatize becomes the furniture. In Moorthy, a young man who enlists in the movement and takes its precepts home to his village, Kanthapura, lives the hero of our time—a career made poignant because the world Raja Rao created is one where, quite literally, gods live with men.

Allow me to give you a feel of the novel with a passage right out of its center—the narrator is an old woman.[11]

Katrik has come to Kanthapura, sister—Katrik has come with the flow of lights and the unpressed footsteps of the wandering gods; white lights from clay trays, and red lights from copper stands, and diamond lights that glow from the bowers of entrance leaves; lights that glow from banana trunks and mango twigs, yellow light behind white leaves, and green light behind yellow leaves, and white light behind green leaves; and night curls through the shadowed streets, and hissing over bellied boulders and hurrying through dallying drains, night curls through the Brahmin street and the Pariah street and the Potter's street and the Weavers' street and flapping through the mango grove, hangs clawed for one moment to the giant pipal, and then shooting across the broken fields, dies quietly into the river— the gods walk by lighted streets, blue gods and quiet gods and bright-eyed gods, and even as they walk in transparent flesh the dust gently sinks back to the earth, and many a child in Kanthapura sits late into the night to see the crown of this god and that, how many a god has chariots with steeds white as foam and queens so bright that the eyes, shut themselves in fear lest they be blinded. Katrik is a month of the gods, and as the gods pass by the Potters' street and the Weavers' street, lights are lit to see them pass by. Katrik is a month of lights, sisters, and in Kantha- pura when the dusk falls, children rush to the sanc- tum flame and the kitchen fire, and with broom grass and fuel chips and coconut rind they peel out fire and light clay pots and copper candelabras and gas lamps. Children light them all, so that when darkness hangs drooping down the eaves, gods may be seen passing by, blue gods and quiet gods and bright-eyed gods. And as they pass by, the dust sinks back into the earth, and night curls again through the shadows of the streets. Oh! have you seen the gods, sister?

Raja Rao enthralls with that kind of language. While copying this text I wondered just where I might drop, with a straggle of dots, a phrase or a sentence, but miserably failed, this being obviously against the wishes of the gods. Incidentally, in *Kanthapura* Raja Rao dealt definitively with the language issue. English, as you know, is only one of several major languages of India, a legacy of Lord Macaulay's, we are told. Like Filipinos, Indians have had this debate on whether Indian-ness is best served by writing in some native language instead of English. As regards his choice of English, Raja Rao writes:

> We are all instinctively bilingual, many of us writing in our own language and in English. We cannot write like the English. We should not. We cannot write only as Indians. We have grown to look at the large world as part of us. Our method of expression therefore has to be a dialect which will some day prove to be as distinctive and colorful as the Irish or the American. Time alone will justify it.[12]

For whatever this might amount to as so much cold water poured over our linguistic nationalism, the fact is that there is now what is called the New Literature in English, and all because numerous writers have emerged from that portion of the world that had had colonial experience from English-speaking masters and have come up with literatures of their own. Foremost among these writers is V.S. Naipaul, whose *A House for Mr. Biswas* is a masterpiece. Here, the colonial having fought his way to the top and acquired an Oxford education, recovers for us the life and times of his family. As a Trinidadian Hindu, Naipaul's central character may well be furniture in a novel about Caribbean journalism were an Englishman around to write it. But Naipaul had other plans for him. He created a memorable image of a man, whose persistence and idealism were his weapons in battling a world that saw him as "unnecessary" and ill-deserving of "accommodation." This is a moving portrait, the work of a son memorializing his father.

Naipaul discarded as furniture the passage from country to metropolis and the initiations of a scholarship boy, which he had been. "Of all my books," he was to say twenty years later, "this is the one closest to me." Listening to a radio version of a particularly humorous episode from the book, Naipaul was in tears, "swamped by emotions I had tried to shield myself from for twenty years."[13]

Perhaps an intelligent innocence, the discovery and recovery of experience, is what will help the writing of more novels from our portion of the Third World. In *Awaiting Trespass*, Linda Ty-Casper has begun rendering the last days of the Marcos regime. Again, by leaving off-stage the violence of the period, this being its furniture, she gives us a memorable Telly and three remarkable Marias of middle-class folklore. These are portraits that will live; whatever its place in the national literature may be, the book will claim its rank in the new literature.

Notes

1. Of James Joyce, Chester G. Anderson (*James Joyce*, p. 6), wrote: "But though he was to live out his life in foreign parts, 'exiled in upon his ego...writing the mystery of himself in furniture', most of the furniture was the Dublin of his childhood and youth."
2. Joshue McClennen, *Masters and Masterpieces of the Short Story* (New York: Holt, Rinehart and Winston, 1957), p. 61.
3. New York: Basic Books, 1967.
4. John Lehmann, *Penguin New Writing*, 32:8.
5. See Bruce King, "The New Literature Versus Flat Earth Fundamentalism, *Chelsea* 46, pp. x-xix. On the lack of interest in Third World Writing in English, the author says: "Our educational institutions and some literary journals are like our leading politicians—proverbial ostriches: They refuse to face the exciting complexity of the modern world. Our schools, universities, and politicians too often proclaim a fundamental American Flat Earthism and behave as if the world revolves around us alone...
6. *Ibid.*
7. Ortega y Gasset, *op. cit.*, p. 2.

8. *Ibid.*
9. King, *op. cit.*, p. xviii.
10. Donald Herdeck, "Introduction," *Botouala* by Rene Maran (London: Heinemann, 1987), p. 3.
11. Raja Rao, *Kanthapura* (New York: New Directions, 1963), p. 81.
12. *Ibid.*, p. vii.
13. V.S. Naipaul, "A Foreword to this Edition," in *A House for Mr. Biswas* (New York: Vintage Books Edition, 1984), p. 1.

6. Towards a National Literature

Some observations on the tension between history and literature, and on a writer-and-subject relationship under a theory of narrative which goes beyond language and cultures, and which may be pressed into service to provide a legacy of feeling.

*I*f song commands a special attention in our culture, might not a musical, say, "Katy!" be regarded as important as a great book? The notion should not be too shocking.

Song is the lifejacket to hand when we get tossed over into the sea of conflict between generations, says Manuel E. Arguilla in "How My Brother Leon Brought Home a Wife"; and what a case in his favor Jose Javier Reyes provides in the musical play.

The play is not so much about a small-town girl who made it to Manila and survived vaudeville, the silent film, then the talkies, and all the years through Japanese Occupation and Liberation, as it is about the period from the mid-twenties to the late forties. An artist has to be a weaver who, laying out his material upon the frame of a loom called Theatre, makes marvelous cloth out of it. In this instance, Mr. Reyes has written a play worthy of mention to the most rabid of admirers of Rizal's *Noli Me Tangere*, though this could be an irreverence for some. Mr. Reyes wrote a play and not a novel; and what he wrote needed actresses and actors, music and stage props, and all the furniture of the drama. But drama has made great strides in the country and to single out one play is to leave out others equally successful, thoughtful, culturally important. All this, though, is by way of saying that we need all the artists that can be found.[1]

Consider the family album as an artifact of our cultural

life. Philippine experience has depended, alas, on the family album technique. There is a coterie of impresarios touchingly devoted to the family photo collection despite the all-too-successful authority of TV in the Filipino living room. Thus the national experience—the confusion and light, the exultation and agony, the frustration and hope we call Philippine life configured into Pre-Spanish, Spanish, Early American, and finally The Present—has been offered to the public as a structure for costuming and nostalgia. Thanks to the word "spectacular," which the ads use, we have survived the banality.

What Mr. Reyes and his theatre have done was dismiss the seamstresses and nostalgia trip, striking out instead for the portrayal of character and the rendering of scene. For honest-to-goodness storytelling, in short. Indeed it is character, scene and drama that compel attention. In this instance, we are given a stereotype that becomes a person living out her allotted block of time, with her aspirations and talents pitted against innumerable odds, and, happily for us, against also a backdrop of colonial history. After this performance we have no need for any history book for a good while, and not because texts are faulty but because drama has powers that historiography does not possess.

History is storytelling also, but it does the work differently. What the historian does is give us what we need to know about the past, to understand the present and project the future intelligently. Yet another kind of storytelling is journalism, where the preferred center is the present in flux. A third, and radically unique, is in literature—in fiction. Being essentially uncommitted to the past, present, and future, fiction is liberated, even irresponsible, especially relative to what lies beyond instruction and entertainment.

But, of course, this is not the greater truth about fiction; its metonymic nature, as in all art, is what we seek and cherish. Fiction attains this capability of offering seeming representations that become in fact the totalities we may just have well already known. This is the reason for the freedom allowed in its making. To claim and exercise it, the writer elevates his construction to a privileged position, a plane tentatively unrelated to the workaday world, freighted with its past, present, and future. It is upon this new and higher ground that he causes the emergence of yet another experience, a reality insulated from our accustomed sense of time and place. Many reading hours later, and having descended to the normal level of space and time, we realize we have been somewhere—a place that was, actually, nowhere—and yet is everywhere. This universality is the gift of achieved art. Our acceptance of it is what Dylan Thomas must have meant when he defined the poem as an addition to reality.

This is central to presenting our experience as a people in terms of the imagined life. This is a transformation which, furthermore, takes on the character of literature—that is to say, an affair of letters (particularly in this respect, unlike drama and film). But how vividly is that experience revealed? Undoubtedly, only as vividly as our talent allows us. How best to press that talent at the service of clarity is the next question.

If in the Philippines the short story has become a favored form, so has the novel even as writers have begun to distinguish between real people and furniture in the so-called house of fiction. It is time to ask: How are we to go about contributing to it?

Keep your eyes on the object. We have been told this repeatedly. But this is easier said than done. Every convention of narratologists yields a harvest of new ways of seeing experience and of telling the world about it. If adding to a national literature is our professed objective, might there be some particularly productive methods?

We would be the last person to propose one, if we exactly knew; but there is perhaps an efficient way of viewing experience so that we may be able to transform it into imagined life—that is to say, writing that is readable and memorable enough. It is a method which, in our view, may be also useful to historians, journalists and all those minded to produce narratives of some kind. Add to the short list all poets, painters, sculptors, scenarists, librettists, and composers —indeed the entire storytelling crowd. The method goes beyond language, discovers its own forms, and honors the verities and the infinitude we call Life.

Consider a horizontal line with three points: A, B, and C. Let us assign the Observer to print A, the Observed to B. To function as Observer, one needs physical as well as moral capability. The same is true with the Observed; it must be formally observable and worthy of attention.

Let us suppose, then, that we have at hand a camera. Its lens is dependable, the shutter sound. Focused on a landscape or an object, the lens may render it faithfully enough. But is visual fidelity all we ask for? Being without any moral or intellectual virtue, the lens cannot be expected to present the scene or object at its best.

Thus, to achieve a landscape with some kind of value— which could say, for example, that our mountains have been ruined by a ruthless neglect of our forest resources—we would need a right-minded environmentalist behind our camera. Such a message, incidentally, amounts to a story.

Because the Observer is equipped with a moral capability, we cannot but have the potential of a story. And a landscape —or any object or phenomenon, for that matter—worthy of observation, an image of it having been created, would have at once a significant story to tell. Worthiness or value diverts our attention elsewhere.

The two points, that of the Observer and that of the Observed, are what we have accounted for so far. But suppose the Observer were a person standing by a roadside, for example; might we not produce a more interesting picture? A depth of field would be registered; the details there could tell us a great deal. It would be very much like seeing more of the truth than what we asked for, as Joseph Conrad would say.

For if the Observer and the Observed belong to the world of the present, the area beyond point B, which we shall henceforth identify as C, is the domain of symbol and myth. They provide the dimension of meaning relevant to, but not co-terminus with, B. The imagination has been engaged and urged to venture beyond—where meanings may go as far as myth and archetype. Thus, in rendering the national experience, we can hardly manage with a poor lens. The capability for registering a depth of field may be all the difference between a superficial and. a profound contribution.

Could it be that perhaps we have used our talent, to date, in the service of recovering merely the experienced reality? Our range of offerings at this level has been remarkable, even as we keep trying out as best as we can, and with varying virtuosity, our control of a received language or our retrieval of one threatened by cavalier neglect and ill-use. But enthusiasm and promptitude may not suffice. There are traps ahead.

For behind the current nationwide debate on how best and how soon to commit Filipino/Pilipino between the shafts—so as to urge the mule of progress aways, instead of merely letting it stand idle, its tail occasionally taking swipes at obstreperous gadflies—is not exactly unrelated to the urgency of rendering our very own story for the world.

For whatever the expressed reasons for championing the native language may be, perhaps deep in our subconscious is the knowledge that our lives belong to some megamyth that needs breaking down into innumerable stories yet to be told, each of them, and then retold, and ever so often again, for generations to come. Sadly, though, we have been at the receiving end of a wash of messages, and in a language yet that we have to command—in order to comprehend that we are being commanded.

We simply have to put an end to the situation. Things are different now. We need to speak out, and then perhaps even redeem ourselves. Which is one big story in itself. Thus we cannot afford to stay too long at our post, as observers of the national experience, holding only a box camera. Even a trouble-free, computerized, self-focusing video camera may not serve.

Sometimes it is, in fact, the equipment that makes the difference. With the right one, an observer is doubly blessed; to the gifted goes even yet greater promise. What is sad to note is that the conditions in the writing community obtaining today are not encouraging; the best of our writers have to make do with dull and old tools, and then are forced into relationships of dependency with patrons, replicating a landlord-peasant situation in the haciendas of information and service industries. Our most promising talents often get hired out on terms more appropriate to coolie labor.

The situation, in other words, has developed where the opportunity for observing the scene, from a point of view informed by valid moral or intellectual virtues, is seldom available to the person qualified. Thus the real objects on the national scene that get singled out for observation are few and far between. Illuminative fiction on or covering various periods of our history, for example, has remained unwritten. For a people with a proud 400-year history, how many titles may we offer for a readable collection? In the few books that we cherish as the best works by Filipinos, what depths of field are revealed?

There has been scant help, moreover, from literary criticism. In this field a long jaded bourgeois sensibility has become dense to insights that our writers provide abundantly. If only critics knew where to look! Writers unaware of this difficulty on the part of their detractors have invariably yielded the field, having themselves forgotten that the writing of criticism is an art, not a version of some gymnastics routine. For their part, many critics have quieted down for lack of hapless victims to browbeat.

As a cultural activity appropriate to a growing nation, the making of literature is thus stumped. And it is not the writer who endures the harm. It is the student, the aspiring intellectual, the serious reader of our cultural history—it is they, since they embody the future, who get hurt. And that future suffers depletion before its time. To pause, to take stock as to which portions of our national experience have been rendered in books, thanks to the discipline of some writers working at their veins of gold, is to be shocked into admission that there are too few of them in each generation who carry on. By way of a cover, we bemoan our lack of readers, the educational system, the national language problem, etc., etc.

All these observations are by way of a fumbling effort, perhaps, at stressing that where we fall short is in imaginative writing. For what is a national literature but a legacy of feeling that the artists amongst us have willed to objectify and leave behind? That feelings have their body and shape is a mystery that Art contributes to our reality. That we have artists in the cultural community for this work is our good fortune.

Time was when the wealth of nations was based on agriculture; the center shifted and, first, Capital, and then Information, became paramount. Power rested with him who knew. But Feeling as Information belongs to the province of Art. Thus, if power belongs to the informed, then to be informed about feelings vaults one to fortune.

Among my souvenirs of a visit to the J.Paul Getty Museum in Los.Angeles is a bookmark depicting a detail of a tabletop constructed about 1600 in Rome. What the per capita national income in Italy at that time was, we can only guess. Enough that we know that the J. Paul Getty Museum honors one of the biggest fortunes ·in America.

The bookmark I refer to represents a lapidary made of semi-precious stones—onyx, cornelian, agate, and lapis lazuli mixed with marbles called *antico nero* and *verde antique.* "To create a bold and stunning effect," said that museum brochure.

Here then, was, firstly, a feeling worthy of expression and, secondly, a Roman artisan's belief that it was worthy of leaving behind. And now this boldness and stunning effect is still very much around: a Roman feeling that has survived four centuries.

What does Roman boldness 400 years ago look like? The question may not be easily comprehensible, but its answer is in the detail of a tabletop made into a bookmark we have described. This is all that Art does. And the wealth of men and nations has been put to its service.

The same good fortune awaits the latest new pages that our writers will add to the national literature.

Notes

1. This was one evening in November 1988. Philippine Long Distance Telephone Co., in cooperation with GR Creative Management Services and the Bigay Pagmamahal Foundation, first presented "Kathy!" at Rizal Theater, Makati, On January 8, 1988, starring Mitch Valdes and Celeste Legaspi.

"As in Myth, the Signs Were All Over": The Fiction of N. V. M. Gonzalez

Richard R. Guzman

Everything, then, can be a myth? Yes, I believe this, for the universe is infinitely fertile in suggestions.

Roland Barthes

Magellan made his fateful landfall in the Philippines at Cebu on March 16, 1521; and, with the signal exception of his slaying some six weeks later, it has seemed possible to read the bulk of Philippine history as a series of capitulations. Politics became Spanish, religion became Spanish (the Islands were an Archdiocese before 1600), and in 1850 when, to ease tax-collecting problems, Governor-General Narciso Claveria decreed that all *indios* be given Spanish surnames, even given names became Spanish. One of the Philippines' greatest modern writers, Nick Joaquin, has said:

> ...there is as great a gulf between the pre-Spanish
> drift of totem-and-taboo tribes and our present
> existence as one people as there is between proto-
> plasm and a humane creature. The *content* of our
> national destiny is ours to create, but the basic *form*,
> the *temper*, the physiognomy, Spain has created for
> us.

Yet I wonder if even Joaquin believes form and content to
be so separable. And what of the Americans, who accomplished in just over half a century a transformation of Philippine culture perhaps more spectacular than Spain managed
in just over three and a half?

In 1900 the Partido Federalista, the first political party
organized under American jurisdiction, had as one of its
planks eventual annexation to the U.S.; and in general Filipinos so embraced American ideals that Americans found it
natural to refer to them as "little brown brothers." So far the
most successful Filipino fiction writer in America has been
Carlos Bulosan, whose 1946 best-selling autobiography was
entitled *America Is in the Heart*.

Naturally, then, many Filipino writers have long been
haunted by the sense of a buried, perhaps irretrievably lost
native past. In the December 1940 issue of *Philippine American News Digest*, journalist P.C. Morante wrote:

> In myself I am often at a loss to account for the
> genuine native. To be sure, I have the physical
> quality of my race; but I feel that the composition of
> my soul is thoroughly soaked with the alien spirit. Of
> course...a great number of my people...are aware that
> even their virtues are borrowed and that their think-
> ing, their dreams and their aspirations have been
> influenced so much by American and Spanish ways
> that the indigenous substance of their true being has
> been crushed or lost.
> ...My actions and reactions, my thoughts and

ideals, even my complexes and inhibitions—all this seems to revolve around a foreign pattern that is easily recognizable as intrinsically of the West.

On the other hand, N.V.M. Gonzalez writes in a recent letter:

At the moment...I'm reading history and a whole ton of it. I can say with some sense of responsibility now that the Filipino today has not changed from the way he was circa 1400!

He is an optimistic man. Born in Romblon, Romblon Island, on Sept. 8, 1915, he turned before his twenties from the study of law to the life of writing, first as a staff at Manila's *Graphic Weekly*. Some of the early years are recounted in his first novel, the autobiographical *Winds of April* (1940), and his turn to writing in "On the Eve," the story which begins his latest volume, *Mindoro and Beyond* (1980). Believing in the efficacy of storytelling and the power of the past, especially of childhood, Gonzalez has, amid heavy demands, also as an influential editor and teacher, produced a body of work that has won all his country's major honors, been translated into several languages, and shown him worthy of being considered among the finest English prose stylists to have come from the Third World. He also makes guitars.

In 1974 he found an old, broken guitar in a junk shop and bought it for $1.50. His account of the incident in a newspaper article titled "Reflections on an Old Guitar" is worth quoting at length.

Some five hours and a half later, along with a roll of paper towels, a couple of brushes, and a quart of denatured alcohol, the box began to reveal its worth.

To be sure, we recognized its mark, "C.F. Martin & Co." branded on wood in 12-point caps, sans serif, followed with "New York" similarly imprinted on the cross-grained center lining of the back. A check with the published records of this maker showed that it was the practice of this firm to place its brand name in two places as well: on the block that joins the neck to the body; and on the back, where the heel joins the body.

Our cleaning job revealed that all but the letters "C" and "N" of the firm name, and the "K" in "New York" had been scraped away....

"For this," said the proprietor of a music shop we visited, "I can give you a real classic guitar, and some cash besides." Forthwith, he took from the rack a signed Yairi guitar worth four hundred dollars...but of course, we had to decline the offer....

Now the responsibility of owning a gem like this one involves not so much material values but ethical and artistic ones. We decided, for example, to undertake the restoration job ourself....But what were we now to do about being faithful to the guitar's original appearance?

...What songs it must have strummed to, no one can tell, but the ebony fingerboard remains to this hour a small monument to perfection. An ambitious repairer had wanted to protect it from wear by varnishing it, which, of course, had been a blasphemy. We had to remove the coat with care, revealing a board on which minor chords had been much favored, judging by the rubbing of the fingertips on the ebony.

Now, the Philippine past is, as it were, the battered guitar. So many things are irretrievably lost, it is true; but Gonzalez' intense, patient devotion to detail and history has seemed to strip so many colonial overlays, to reveal clues—some as subtle as the rubbings of fingertips but powerful enough to impel the ethical and artistic urge to restore. Gonzalez says he has even found a transcendent reason for the Philippine peasant's seemingly easy acceptance of his landlord's usury:

The acceptance of the practice [of doubling unpaid debts], I now seem to understand, was (and is) not traditional but transcendental. For exactly the same practice was observed in pre-Spanish Philippines, the logic of those times being this: that when a measure of rice was planted, harvest rewarded the effort at the least a hundredfold. The "dublihan" practiced then was actually generous. It is this sense of generosity that appears to have transcended time....Perhaps it is the nobility of the peasantry that has allowed its members to acquiesce to the practice...and the gentry's sense of guilt that has led it to devise other means of exploitation.

He is, as I have said, an optimistic man. Yet under the continuing scrutiny of sociology, anthropology, and history a unique—and, yes, "transcendent"—Philippine past is rapidly disclosing itself; and the Philippines even possess, after all, a somewhat respectable, if fragmented, revolutionary tradition complete with mystic overtones and fiery, colorful leaders who moved their people to stand against a multitude of foreign indignities. Gonzalez' optimism is not, in short, mere optimism. It, too, is severely tempered by that dark sense of loss and concession that haunts the best Filipino writers. But in most instances Gonzalez is able to balance cultural pessimism and personal optimism so tightly that his works are generally, though not completely, free both from the facile hope and melodrama romanticism that otherwise plague a literature so obsessed with its people's lost identity. Furthermore, while he is a master of high drama, Gonzalez' very prose style works against the overly dramatic, the imbalanced. "Every volume since Gonzalez' first," writes the American critic Leonard Casper,

> is so noticeably underwritten that he runs the risk of being misread, of having subtleties overlooked, of leaving unmoved those readers used to bathos.

Such restraint is the product of a vision which blends detail and history with pattern and cosmos. Gonzalez' narrative style intends to deemphasize the forward-moving, the linear, in favor of a complex, often near-static time frame, a frame which seems to shimmer gently as Gonzalez moves easily, with minimal transitions, between past, present, and future, between conscious time and the less-metered times of memory, dream, hallucination, or reflection. In turn, this handling of time makes more natural the creation of confluences between the realm of myth and the minutiae of daily living. Besides its restraint and complex timing, what typically impresses the reader of Gonzalez' work first is its abundant and lovingly given detail. More than any other Philippine writer, Gonzalez concerns himself with names, with the building of houses, the catching of fish, the harvesting of rice, the sharpening of knives used in that harvest. Then in the midst of detail will often come a kind of time warp making us realize that certain facts, certain rhythms of action, somehow rise from some ancient memory, some cosmic pattern, and, more important, have the potential of con- necting us to those things from which they arise.

Gonzalez' best works are thus significant ventures in mythmaking, or, more precisely, countermythmaking. For a society establishes meaning and interprets its history by dint of its myths, those signs and stories which seem to it to be immemorial; and it is the seemingly timeless, dehistoricized, depoliticized naturalness of myth which creates the illusion of naturalness in any given social order, any given history. Myth, then, is a kind of metahistory, the very premise of historical constructions. In essence, the writer who proposes really to "re-vision" history must offer us a countermyth, must select new facts, images, actions for elevation to a transcendent plain or create narrative contexts in which old material takes on new meaning. It is in countering the myths of the Philippines' irretrievably lost native past, of her people's weakness, of the near-total triumph of the foreign that Gonzalez' fiction is unique. Such countering is most beautifully realized in *A Season of Grace*, his masterpiece, and surely one of the four or five most beautiful novels to have come from the Third World.

II

THE novel revolves around the contrasting of two couples who live on the island of Mindoro. One couple is Epe and Tiaga Ruda, the establishment, the supervisors, the people of means to whom others become beholden. The other couple is Doro and Sabel Agnas, poor folk who leave the Rudas' employ to seek a life for themselves on a frontier farm, or *kaingin*. Their life is hard. Crops often fail:

> There was a week when they lived on nothing but mushrooms; and there was the week of the bamboo shoots, which tasted quite all right, pickled in vinegar that Blas Marte's wife sent over.
> Still, can one go on that way? The thought was like a temptation. It said further: Leave the clearing for once! And, mouse-like, it gnawed at Sabel's mind.

Gonzalez does not at all romanticize their hard lives, yet it is impossible not to sense that, because of the sharing among the poor folk and because of their closeness to the earth, people like Doro and Sabel maintain vital connections to those elemental rhythms of life that sustain communion and make them more whole. For the Rudas, especially Tiaga, the story is different. They are *not* portrayed as villains. Rather, because they are unconnected with the earthy rhythms of planting and harvest, they also partake only superficially in real sharing with people. They are lonely, and one notices in Tiaga a growing paranoia which is accompanied by an increasingly frantic rhythm in her movements and speech. In the end, in contrast to Sabel, we also confirm the fact of Tiaga's physiological infertility as we learn, sadly, of her third miscarriage.

A Season of Grace—which consists of a prologue, epilogue, and three long, unnumbered chapters—follows the

Rudas, Agnas, and others through just over one cycle of planting and harvest. Yet the feeling of time is expansive, so much so that the *Philippines Free Press* reviewer described the book as

> ...a poem about an island—and so full of myth-making images that it recovers for Mindoro—poor island with a wondrous name—something of the mystery...with which the conquistadores and the early navigators saw it.

This feeling of expansive mythmaking comes largely from those things previously mentioned: Gonzalez' handling of time, his constant recourse to the memories and dreams and reflections of his characters. It comes, too, from a lyricism in the narrative voice and speech of the Philippine peasant which laces the story with poetry. Thus the first chapter begins:

> Man and woman were walking one morning in the sun down a trail that cut across the bed of the empty river Alag.
> The woman carried a baby, using a hammock slung over her shoulder. The cloth was the same piece of catcha which last night had served as her little one's blanket. The baby whimpered inside the hammock-pack: the woman couldn't seem to make him quiet. The man said:
> "Why don't you fix it, Sabel, so that it will not hurt?" He wanted to add: "Is it heavy like a yoke?" But he realized that she looked pretty enough with that hammock-pack; it was quite an ornament.
> "Doro," the woman said, "please have the kindness to wait for us."
> Whereupon Doro stopped and looked back. Without either slowing down or hurrying, Sabel lifted her hammock-pack a little and began rubbing the back of her neck with her palm, hoping in some way perhaps to relieve the strain there.
> Doro was all the more reminded of the yoke.

This had been a carabao's trail. Now it was a man's trail. Ferns raised their arched fronds on all sides and a patch of cogon stood now a little way off to the right, waving bright tassels in the sun.

Or, when Sabel first arrives at a harvest site, we read:

Sabel was about to go when she saw a girl in the hut, seated in the middle of the floor. The girl's dress had been dyed with tanbark so that it was dark brown, like the thatched wall behind her.

Without any shyness, the girl asked: "You are Manang Sabel?"

Surprised, Sabel said: "Yes. How did you know my name?"

"Someone will come from over across the dry bed of the Alag, I was told. Someone with a baby, and she will be called Sabel, they·said."

Sabel pondered for a moment. She liked the girl for being talkative.

In the first passage the near-Biblical tone quickly gives way to a scene of domestic friction, which in turn alternates with Doro's reflections, some selfish ("she looked pretty enough"), some which ponder the mythic yoke. We have, too, a restatement of the man-animal-plant hierarchy which Gonzalez had established early in the prologue to give us the feeling, present here, that man and animal make their way through life by the grace of the earth and its vegetation. The color of dress and thatch in the second passage suggests again the man-earth bond, but more noteworthy is the tone of the girl's reply to Sabel. That tone itself, one feels, might send Sabel searching through her memory. Indeed, she does just this shortly. For now, though, she pauses—ponders—on the verge and is quickly called back by a commonplace: she likes the girl's "talkativeness."

Such passages abound in *A Season of Grace*, and most (like the scene of a dream and lovemaking following a day of clearing the fields in chapter three) weave together the domestic and mythic, the memorial and mundane in extraordinarily beautiful and complex ways. In such a stylistic atmosphere so many images become mythmaking, become—or seem on the verge of becoming—transmuted upward into timeless signs that give meaning to history. Whether it is an object (like a coconut), an action (the weaving of buri mats), or a relation (between Filipino manual labor and American mechanical harvesters, for example), one feels in Gonzalez' work a subtle, gentle, yet monumental retooling of signs for different ends. Let us take, for example, the coconut.

For a multitude of historical, commercial, and geothermal reasons the coconut has long been associated with the Islands. My brother, Jose Enrado, was given (for reasons I could not then fathom) the nickname "Coconut Joe." And a recent TV commercial tells us that company X is bringing the coconut halfway around the world—"From the Philippines!"—as a guarantor of moist skin. In *A Season of Grace* its function is less cosmetic.

Early in the novel a coconut is found and planted, and though there are other references to it throughout, it is only near the end of the book that its full meaning becomes apparent.

> ...(Nay Kare) was standing, her feet wet, not more than ten yards from him. The coconut she had picked up looked small in the crook of her arm. Its husk glistened more than ever now that it was out of the water, a rich dark brown that was the color of one's skin.
>
> Doro walked up to her. "Will that ever grow, Nay Kare?" he asked, although what really crossed his mind was: "What wind and wave have sent it to this shore?"
>
> "Why, yes, of course. You can ask Sabel."
>
> Her patadiong wet against her breast and hips and legs, Sabel stepped out of the water, saying: "Yes, I remember. The one you picked up last time—

why, it has sprouts already, I believe. And Doro," she assured him, "we planted it at once and it grew."

"Soaked in salt water as it was?" Doro could not believe her.

..."How else do you thing can coconuts go from island to island?" Nay Kare said, "Oh, well, let's be on our way."

Because so much of the book has concerned the poor folk going from clearing to clearing, island to island, working in the saltwater sweat of their brows for whatever the earth will yield, one realizes that the coconut is a metaphor for the Philippine peasant's survival and growth—but not only that. It is a sign meant to re-vision history by joining together certain qualities of a people with certain other historical facts about that people's creation.

Except for the Negritos (themselves relatives of the natives of the Australian bush), the Philippine people are an amalgam of travelers. A Philippine village, in fact, is called by a name that suggests not settlement, but journey: it is *barangay*, the name of a coconut-tough little boat on which many arrived from Polynesia, Malaysia, Micronesia, China, the Indian sub-continent. Philippine history, then, is shaped largely by those who arrive. This includes the white man, too, and thus *A Season of Grace* begins with an epigraph from *New Voyage Around the World* by the English seaman and pirate William Dampier (1652-1715). "The 18 Day of Feb." it begins, "we anchored at the N.W. end of the island of Mindora, in 10 Fathom-Water, about 3 quarters of a Mile from the Shore. Mindora is a large island...."

"Will that ever grow?" asks Doro. Some travelers come, plant themselves, and grow—some do not, either because they do not really plant, or because, like the corrupt officials in *A Season of Grace* who take buri mats from Sabel in the beginning and Clara at the end, they are flagrant robbers. Those qualities which do spur growth Gonzalez wants to identify as the spine of Philippine character, the essence of a genuinely native past. They show most clearly, though certainly not without a great deal of tarnish, in the generosity, patience, and nobility of the Philippine peasant. The coconut becomes a mythic sign as it links the qualities of peasant life and the historical origins of Philippine society to its own immemorial travel and endurance of the salty sea. In many quarters of the Southeast Asian world the coconut is, of course, an already sacred sign; what Gonzalez adds to it is a new, pointed historicity. He uses it, that is, to reshape subtly, but significantly, an old story; and thus the fruit of the palm goes beyond even its more significant meanings, to say nothing of the way it surpasses its other familiar function as a sign of the carefree, exotic tropics, of Coconut Joes and luscious complexions. It helps make "natural" that generosity, patience, and nobility which makes more likely the overcoming of the hardships of travel, landing, and growth—or, more important here, the overcoming of colonialism.

In a recent lecture at the University of Hawaii, Gonzalez speculated that in terms of the literary imagination the Comic Rhythm might be the best way for the Third World to deal with the historical circumstances of imperialism; for the Comic Rhythm celebrates community, integration, the overcoming of fragmenting alien spirits. *A Season of Grace* leaves the Rudas inclining toward the Tragic Rhythm, toward loneliness and disintegration. The poor folk, for all their faults and the often desperate straits of their lives, incline toward the comic. In fact, the novel ends with a joke which involves not only a sailing ship but rice, one of the book's most crucial, mythic signs. In the epilogue Tata Pablo, the first villager we meet in the book's prologue, is slowly going blind, and his wife, Nay Rosa, searches an old almanac to find an appropriate saint to pray to:

> Nay Rosa, unused to the weight of paper in her hand, could not keep her arm from trembling. "*Tiempo variable*, it says," she said. "And after the first quarter of the moon, clear skies with light winds from

the southwest."

Tata Pablo blinked his eyes and leaned forward, turning his head a little to one side. "Louder."

"I need better light," Nay Rosa said moving toward the door.

"All right. Go on, though. What does it say about the southwest monsoon?"

"Nothing more, it seems," Nay Rosa said. "Can I look now for a name of that saint?"

"It's now a week since the batel came and loaded Epe Ruda's rajitas."

"Exactly a week. Don't you think it's San Juan?"

"I don't know. 'San Juan for the blind?'—that doesn't seem familiar," the old man said. "Was it a big batel?"

"With two masts," said Nay Rosa. "Maybe, it's San Pablo."

"It seems I can still hear the sound of the pulleys when the men hoisted up their sails," Tata Pablo said. "It was painted white?"

"White like boiled rice," Nay Ròsa said, putting down the *Almanaque Panayana*. "Maybe, it's San Lorenzo."

"You make me hungry—thinking of rice," Tata Pablo said. "Try another saint."

Against the failing crops, of dreams, even of eyesight, such an attitude is strangely powerful. At its best, Gonzalez' mythmaking moves to this comic rhythm. It is one of the most steady, hopeful rhythms in Third World literature. The native culture will survive, it seems to say, and by an inner strength that antedates colonialism.

III

Until some enlightened U.S. publisher takes it on, *A Season of Grace* is available as an inexpensive import from The

Cellar Bookshop (in Detroit at 18090 Wyoming). Now at least the University Press of Hawaii is making available Gonzalez' latest book, *Mindoro and Beyond: 21 Stories*. In part, the book is a retrospective collection culled from 40 years' work. It contains some of the Third World's finest short stories— "Lupo and the River," "Children of the Ashcovered Loam," "The Sea Beyond," "On the Ferry," "The Wireless Tower," "The Tomato Game"—and Gonzalez has arranged them not only to reflect a growing range of concern (symbolized by the distance between Mindoro and the U.S.) but also to parallel his abiding interest in the act of storytelling itself. (Coincidentally—or maybe not—the stories also fall roughly in chronological order.) In the book's preface Gonzalez reproduces this passage from one of his notebooks:

> It is because of our access to storytelling that the confusions and the incomprehensible realities round and about do not overwhelm us with despair. We find in due course a way of ordering the experience we go through (as, indeed, others do), and somehow come to understanding Reality as we live it—until swamped once more by fresh confusions and perplexities. Then comes a new surge of hope, and, again for him who must give an account of how things are, a search for form.

Several of Gonzalez' characters can be taken as symbols of the artist, the storyteller. Twenty-five years ago Francisco Arcellana singled out this passage from "Lupo and the River" in order to praise Gonzalez' own craftsmanship:

> Lupo taught him (Pisco) how to work the rattan this way and that, never sacrificing pattern for strength, never losing your purpose, and yet taking care to make out of something ordinary a beautiful thing.

Significantly, Sabel, in *A Season of Grace*, is a mat maker whose habit it is to weave the word *Recuerdo*—"Remember" —into the center of her design. As she works with buri, so

Gonzalez the writer can be seen working words, weaving on the warp and woof of myth and detail stories which declare to his people that there is indeed some unique past, something worth remembering.

Mindoro and Beyond, then, begins with the semiautobiographical "On the Eve," about a young man's decision to become a writer, and the book ends with an historical essay on Philippine storytelling, followed by an often whimsical glossary of Philippine terms. As "On the Eve" begins, Greg Padua is a proofreader for Commonwealth Publishing Co. His father is a salesman. Says Padua:

> As proofreader, with lines of type before my eyes, or galleys in my hand, my commitment was to the present. It is now rather easy to see things in this light. I stood for the text of the day, Father the pages of tomorrow.

As he moves toward the literary life, however, he realizes, as he says, that "I was transgressing my commitment to the present, that I was in fact making a dubious step to the future, a territory of promises...." One Mr. Campo, as the editor of a company named "Commonwealth" might be expected to do, rebukes Padua's poetic ambitions. Padua quits his job, as well as his nighttime study of law, and as the story ends is handing his father a folder of his short stories and poems. His father is uncomprehendingly silent, and Padua tells us: "The Chinese fiddle across the street began once more to wring its heart out. Father and I had changed places."

Very early in the story Padua had listened to that fiddle and told us:

> My untrained ear could not grasp the melody, which resembled tortured cries and yearnings; but I imagined that it told some enchanting story inspired by the exotic aroma of narra wood and the unarticulated patience of the lives round and about....

It seems as if, in this 1970 story, Gonzalez were summarizing the inspiration, mission, and pattern of growth of virtually his entire literary output. The stories in *Mindoro and Beyond*, which are grouped in six sections, may in fact be seen as growing in melodic complexity and evocativeness. "On the Eve" comprises Part One. In Part Two are pieces from the late thirties, some of which are more sketches than full-bodied stories. As melodies they are simple, with a folk song-like depth and transparency. In Part Three, given the growing complexity of Gonzalez' handling time, the stories begin to resemble a kind of frozen music. And the music darkens. One critic has pointed out that "The Sea Beyond," which ends Part Three, shows how man, though he may overcome the evil in nature, cannot overcome the evil within himself. Part Four consists of the long story "Serenade," which ends with the main character, Pilar, contemplating her new piano,

> a brooding presence that made the moment alive once more with the music that Pilar knew by heart— "Love and Devotion," "Flower Song," "Poet and Peasant"—music with which she must learn to woo the world into being less harsh and, perhaps, less rude.

(The songs here are highly appropriate to themes which span Gonzalez' entire work.) In Part Five, tensions between and within individuals begin merging more noticeably with the theme of tensions between cultures, especially the culture based more upon the Americanized, Hispanized "city." Yet Part Five ends with "The Wireless Tower," which paradoxically images both a total breakdown of communication (the tower, a radio tower, has been struck by lightning) and a celebration of the light and dark sides of life—both personal life, and, one presumes, cultural life as well. It is by striving to understand the inextricable entanglements of light and dark, good and evil, victory and concession, that communication might one day be restored. Yet this must surely be the hardest of human tasks.

"Dear Greg" (Greg Padua?), begins "The Tomato Game," the first story in Part Six: "You must believe me when I say that I've tried again and again to write this story."

Two of the six stories in Part Six take place in America, and this setting accentuates virtually every conflict that has appeared thus far in the book. Clearly Gonzalez has had to struggle hard for the momentary victories afforded by art. "As in myth," the writer in "The Tomato Game" says,

> the signs were all over. The wooden bridge, the fork of the road, the large track all around us which earlier had been a tomato field, the rich crops as indicated by the harvesting machine to one side of the field, a menacing hulk....You can see how hard I try.

This passage puts us in direct contact with Gonzalez' effort to re-vision history by creating alternate mythic possibilities. Here the mechanical harvester, so devastating to the manual labor in which Filipinos played so large a part, is reshaped into a sign of technology's inability to eliminate the human factor. It does a bad harvesting job, finally. It is also linked metaphorically to certain unscrupulous Filipinos who engage in bride-selling schemes. Their victim this time is an elderly Filipino, who, though victim, rises in character above his conniving compatriots. His generosity, patience, and nobility clearly link him to those people and ancient qualities celebrated in *A Season of Grace*.

It has been Gonzalez' aim to foster such links through art; and he has realized that one of the greatest obstacles to establishing a nourishing relationship with the past is that that past is, in Robert Frost's words, so "unstoried, artless, unenhanced." Or, perhaps, it is just wrongly storied. The problem with the main character in "In the Twilight," the last story in the book, is that he has lived so long remembering a key incident in his life incorrectly. He literally has the wrong story. A fiddle player in his youth in the Philippines, he is now, in America, "Dan," a jazz saxophonist. The character through whom he inadvertently learns the truth was a Philippine guerrilla. Now he is a security guard—Union Carbide, night shift—hoping for U.S. citizenship in three years. Such transformations are jarring; they seem too forced for a story otherwise so delicately crafted. Yet such changes, especially in music, seem common among Filipinos in America. "In the Twilight" is a somber echo of "On the Eve," but even amid darkening sounds and shadows Gonzalez seems to suggest that a more accurate memory of the past would help his people define who they are as a people and thus be less prone to such far strayings and cultural pessimisms. His message is still *Recuerdo*. But facts take us only so far: we live in a world of contending stories, of myth and countermyth. What a writer ultimately says is, Remember *my* vision of our past. This is the great artist's privilege and obligation. "Unhappily, the spiritual welfare of this country depends upon the fate of its creative minds," wrote Van Wyck Brooks of the American situation in 1918.

> If they cannot grow and ripen, where are we going
> to get new ideals....Discover, invent a usable past we
> certainly can, and that is what a vital criticism always
> does.

Thoughts like these reach obsessive proportions in the Third World, for there artists and critics face baldly redemptive and recreative relationships to native pasts which have been pressed so hard, sometimes so nearly annihilated, by the colonial experience. Fortunately for the Philippines, Gonzalez' vision—even in its twilight, somber hues—is strong, complex, and daringly hopeful.